Machines That Built America

Machines
That Built America

ROGER BURLINGAME

NEW YORK

HARCOURT, BRACE & WORLD, INC.

LIBRARY OF CONGRESS CATALOG CARD NUMBER: 53-10468
PRINTED IN THE UNITED STATES OF AMERICA

Acknowledgments

MY SPECIAL thanks are due the staffs of the Yale University Library and the Engineering Societies Library of New York for help in historical and technological research. Mr. F. Ivor D. Avellino of the American History Division and Mr. T. R. Thomson of the Technology Division of the New York Public Library have been of constant assistance. Mr. Henry E. Edmunds, Mr. Owen Bombard and Mr. Stanley Graham of the Archives Department of the Ford Motor Company made available to me some new material for my chapter "The Finished Map." I am grateful to Mr. Clair M. Elston of The Collins Company for an instructive and pleasant visit to Collinsville, Connecticut, and to Bernice and Walter Gilkyson for their hospitality on that occasion.

Out of the large number of books I have consulted I should like to mention three which were of special value: *The World of Eli Whitney* by Jeannette Mirsky and Allan Nevins, *Oliver Evans, A Chronicle of Early American Engineering* by Greville and Dorothy Bathe and *The History of the Colt Revolver* by Charles T. Haven and Frank A. Belden.

Particular thanks go to Gloria Lubin for expert assistance on the index.

Contents

Machines That Built America

CHAPTER ONE

The Democracy of Things

A FRENCHMAN who had been in the United States only a week was driving in his American friend's car. It was his first visit to this country of which he had heard so many extraordinary accounts. Now, as he looked out at the real thing, his mind was busy trying to fit what he saw into the picture his imagination had drawn. On the outskirts of a river town, he put his hand on the American's arm and asked him to stop a moment.

"Yes," said the American, following his friend's eye, "that is a machine tool factory—one of the oldest in the state."

"I wasn't looking at the factory. I was surprised at the number of cars in that public parking lot."

"It isn't exactly a public parking lot," the American corrected. "It belongs to the factory."

"But the cars?"

"They belong to the employees."

"But how can there be so many superintendents?"

"No, the cars belong to the workers. Machinists, founders,

oilers. The unskilled workers, too."

"But they are big, high-powered cars. They are not like our economical little Citroëns. They are as good as your own—as expensive, no?"

"Better, some of them," said the American. "For instance, from here I can see two Cadillacs, a Packard and a Buick. Of course many of them were bought as used cars."

"But the fuel—the maintenance—the taxes. Imagine factory employees having such luxuries!"

"We do not think of a car as a luxury. It is a necessity. Many of these men and women live at a distance. How could they get to work without cars?"

"In Europe," the Frenchman replied, "they ride bicycles. Or they go on busses. A superintendent may have his car. But it will be a small, low-powered machine which will travel thirty of your miles on a gallon of fuel."

They drove on, then, through the poorer part of the big, sprawling industrial town. To the American this was not a part of his native scene of which he was particularly proud and he wanted to hurry through it. But the Frenchman was surprised and impressed here, too. He kept looking at the roofs of the houses.

"The aerials," he said.

"Yes. Television."

"But these are slums, are they not? How can the people who live here afford such a luxury?"

"Television is not a luxury in America. You buy it on the installment plan—a little down, a little every month for a long time."

"Still it is a luxury. To be able to sit in your home and

see something that is going on in some far distant place is pure luxury. I am told these people also own refrigerators, washing machines and oil burners with automatic heat control."

"Yes, many of them do."

"Of course all those things exist in Europe. But they are owned by people whose parents and grandparents were accustomed to luxuries. As for the others—well, even if a worker should accumulate quite a bit of money, he would somehow not think of owning a car or television. It is a matter of tradition."

This kind of conversation takes place every day as foreigners visit the United States. They are not especially impressed with our knowledge of technics or our understanding of applied science or our craftsmanship. They have magnificent industrial establishments at home which turn out the highest quality of products from jet airplanes to high-fidelity phonograph records. European inventions such as the Bessemer and open-hearth steel processes, the internal combustion engine, radar, the photo-electric cell, synthetic drugs, fertilizer and explosive processes and a hundred others have been essential to American development. Even the automobile was invented in Europe and reached an advanced stage of development there while we were still driving "horseless buggies" with whip sockets on their dashboards. So our American machines and gadgets attract little attention by themselves. The thing the visitor from abroad cannot understand is that "everyone" here seems able to own some beautiful product of all this technology.

Their surprise becomes understandable to us when we travel abroad. To the observant American—although at first things look much the same, especially in the cities—the great differences are soon evident. We are impressed, for instance, by the sharp contrasts between the old and the new. Side by side with the latest development in streamlined travel we will see means of transportation which have not changed in a thousand years. Again and again in the small country villages we will see beautiful, low-slung, high-speed sports cars held up by an ox-drawn wagon or a donkey cart or by lines of women carrying heavy-laden baskets on their heads.

Americans who, in the war, have come to know the farms in France and Italy, remember that, often, there is no electricity; that water comes from a hand pump in the yard; cooking is done on a coal or charcoal stove. We know that there are poverty-stricken sections of this country suffering the same privations, but poverty is not always the cause in Europe. Often the farmer who goes without what we call common comforts is prosperous enough. He may have saved a good sum to pass on to his son or to give his daughter for a dowry when she marries. But plumbing, bathtubs, electricity, heating, automatic water pumps and motor cars are simply not the custom of his social level. And because, traditionally, such things—like butlers, cooks and chauffeurs —belong to the wealthy or to some especially privileged class, they are not produced in sufficient quantity for ordinary folk to be able to buy them.

A trip abroad is, to observant Americans, an extremely valuable experience. At home we are likely to take the extraordinary mechanical marvels which ease our existence for granted. A boy or girl born, say, in the late 1930's or early '40's has never known any other way of life. Even his parents may not remember a time when there was no car in the family; his grandfather must tell what it was like to have no electricity or telephone in his home. We seem to have come into a world which was ready-made for us, which functions perfectly in every detail and requires no effort on our part. The lights spring up at the flick of a switch, an exact temperature is maintained by the setting of a thermostat, the food we need today or shall need months from now is on the shelves in cans or below zero in the home freezer. To press a button releases the power of a hundred and sixty horses to transport us a hundred or a thousand miles without the need of any muscular activity beyond the light touch of the hand on steering wheel or gear shift or the foot on the brake. But in other countries we see all round us the great physical exertion which was demanded of our ancestors to secure the bare necessities of life.

We need the sharp visual contrast we find abroad or in some remote rural part of the United States, such as the Cumberland or Ozark mountains, to wake us to the immense gap between the common life of today and that of a century ago. Immediately our minds are flooded with questions. First: How was this development possible over the huge area of our country which, when the republic started, was mostly wilderness? Second: Why have all these things which are luxuries abroad become commonplaces in the United States, owned by people at almost every level of income? Many other questions follow on these two, once we begin to look into history, and some of the easy answers that first suggest themselves are no longer good enough when we discover the facts of our national growth.

The commonest answer is phrased in the two words: Yankee ingenuity. There is a widespread belief that, from the beginning, Americans were born mechanical geniuses. According to this theory even in colonial times every other boy was an inventor from the age of ten up and became absorbed in scientific study as soon as he could read. This idea seems to have resulted from thinking backward. Because in 1953, American boys are handy with tools, are effective trouble-shooters with all sorts of machines and are often apt pupils in mathematics, physics and chemistry, it is assumed that this was always true.

History, however, shows the exact opposite. While there were, as we shall see, certain highly intelligent and inventive American minds, they were extremely few and so far between that communication was impossible among them. When the republic began there were *even fewer* active inventors than there had been when the states were colonies. The reason for this was that as soon as the independence of the United States was achieved, everyone who could moved west to settle the wild lands and become a farmer. Among the first to go were the mechanics, the men skilled in the use of tools, carpenters, metal workers and blacksmiths. One reason for this was that these people were better able to buy land. In any case they went: they moved away from the coastal cities in droves and when they had reached the frontiers they became wholly absorbed in the work of clearing, plowing and planting and in the resulting prosperity.

The result was that throughout the young United States there was an almost complete dearth of skilled artisans of all kinds. In the letters and diaries of the few great inventors like Eli Whitney we keep coming across references to "the low state of the mechanick arts." Whitney had to abandon his important invention, the cotton gin, because he could not find enough skilled workers to build this simple machine in sufficient quantity to make it profitable. In every branch of technics, America was far behind England. No American could design or construct the kind of machine, for instance, that was bringing tremendous wealth to British capitalists through spinning, weaving and other textile operations. More than forty years after Watt invented the steam engine, Robert Fulton had to buy a British engine to supply power to his *Clermont* because Americans had never properly learned the art of engine building. Almost all steel and most iron were imported. Coal which had been one of the factors of the English industrial revolution was unknown here. Tools came from England, Sweden and Germany. We had no canals, practically no roads. The power for our grist-mills, saw-mills, rolling and slitting mills, our forges and foundries was all water power.

The few American inventors of that period—from 1790, say, to 1810—could find no one interested enough in new mechanical ideas to back them. John Fitch, the true inventor of the steamboat, died in poverty and despair because neither capitalists nor the government would take any interest in his invention. Oliver Evans, one of the greatest of them all, had to fight against ignorance, superstition and blind prejudice to induce millers to adopt his revolutionary flour-milling machinery. With his steam engines and his "road carriage"—a steam automobile—he had even less success. When Charles Newbold patented an iron plow in 1797, farmers refused to use it because they were convinced that the iron would "poison the soil."

It was from this beginning, then, not from the springboard of "Yankee ingenuity" that the United States took off on a career which brought the nation to world leadership in industry. The start, we see, was far behind scratch. We had first to catch up with the rest of civilization in our understanding of technics before we could begin to compete.

Along with this handicap, however, there were other things which aided us. One, oddly enough, was that very westward push which had robbed us of our mechanics and skilled artisans. The migration into the wilderness was on such a vast scale that the needs of these pioneer people out in the empty land suddenly became great. For the first work of clearing forests, "breaking up" and plowing prairie land and building crude temporary log cabins, only axes, mattocks, augers and hand saws, and a few farm implements were needed. But once farmers were fairly started, the work of planting and harvesting the tremendous crops they were able to raise on the virgin soil and of marketing them, left little time for hunting, tanning, cobbling, spinning and weaving which, in their first years on the frontier, the pioneer families had done. It was then, when they were settled and producing, when the first prosperity had come from their crop sales to eastern markets, that the westerners began to want every kind of manufactured goods: cloth, shoes, hardware, glass, flour, clocks, and a hundred other things for the refinement of life in an established community.

At first, when the Revolutionary War was over, it looked as if Americans would continue to import many of those things from abroad as they had done in colonial days. In that time England had done her best to prevent manufacturing in the colonies lest it cut into her own trade. The whole colonial idea, according to English thinking, was for the colonies to grow food, tobacco and such raw materials of manufacture as cotton, indigo and iron for the mother country and to buy from her all their manufactured goods. The laws passed by the English Parliament to enforce this procedure were among the causes of discontent which ended in the fight for independence. But then, even after the Americans had won their liberty, England still tried to prevent factories from starting in the United States. One way of doing this was to flood the country with English goods at far lower prices than the inexperienced Americans could make them. So, for a time, ship after ship unloaded in American ports bales and boxes and barrels of fancy cotton, linen, silk and woolen cloth, leather goods, hardware, clothing, hats—all the things the expanding country needed at such tempting prices and with such easy credit that it was difficult even for the disapproving American patriots to resist buying.

It looked, then, as if the birth of American industry might be indefinitely delayed. In the first place, most of the people did not want factories. Horrible stories of conditions in the "dark Satanic mills," as the great English textile factories

were called, had crossed the Atlantic. Long hours, child
labor in hot, ill-ventilated buildings, starvation wages and
other reputed privations were things to which Americans
were unaccustomed. The outdoor hardships of the frontier
were far more to their liking. The freedom of the wild
lands, teeming with game; the excitement of life in the
woods with its challenge of Indians and wild animals, and
the pleasures of farming in rich soil were far more appeal-
ing than confined labor in spinning and weaving establishments, furnaces and forges. Yet at the same time, to wise
and patriotic men whose thoughts were often far in the
future, the notion of continued dependence on Britain was
intolerable. Alexander Hamilton was such a patriot; so
were Franklin and Tench Coxe and others in New England, New York, Pennsylvania and Delaware of whom we
shall presently hear.

The infant nation, in those days perilously learning its
first steps and making many painful mistakes in the process,
was finally saved by events abroad. By 1800, most of Europe
had been plunged into war. The French Revolution had
been followed by the sweeping conquests of Napoleon.
British and French trade with America had come to an end.
The United States was then truly thrown on its own. Its
only hope was to produce—as much and as fast as possible.
It must make every sort of thing it had previously imported.
It must make its own cloth—not merely with the spinning
wheels and hand looms at home, but on a big enough scale
to supply the wants of people who had acquired tastes in
foreign factory-made cottons and woolens. It must make
shoes, axes, plows, farm implements, guns, buttons, nails,
shovels, chisels, pottery, paper, rope, wagons and carriages,

pots and kettles, stoves, pewter and silverware, gloves, printing presses, hats and stockings on an increasingly large scale as the civilization of the east moved west.

It was soon obvious that these things could not be made by the few, inefficient artisans and mechanics who were left behind after the first tremendous westward rush. *Some substitute must be found for the missing men.* It was then that it occurred to the handful of great mechanical geniuses that were scattered through the coastal states to replace hand labor with machines. Machines must be invented each of which would take the place of ten or fifty or a hundred of the missing men. Somehow a man's skill in carving, cutting, forging, bending, shaping, drilling—a hundred other operations which had been painfully performed by a hand-held chisel or knife or gimlet—must be put into a machine which would run along more or less automatically and turn out the things in great quantity while a boy stood by to watch and occasionally fix something which went wrong.

Soon this business of inventing machines began to spread —especially in New England. As the demand grew for every kind of manufactured thing, men began to compete in ingenuity. Gradually more and more people became absorbed in machine production and fewer in farming. Factories, springing up along the rivers in the East, using the power of the moving water to turn the water-wheels which turned the machines, attracted many men and boys who might otherwise have been swallowed up by the frontier farms. Finally, when steam came, factories sprang up in the West, too, behind the frontiers, where it was easier to supply the settlers who were making their little rural communities into thriving towns and busy cities. In time, those towns were all tied together by the network of railroads, and manufacturing was carried on everywhere.

It is important to remember, therefore, that machine production began in the United States, not because there were so many mechanically skilled people but because there were so few. Machinery was an absolute necessity in America. For this reason machine production was quite different in the United States from what it had been in England where there was too much, not too little, labor. It had come to England first because there was such a high level of scientific knowledge and education and so many inventors who were not diverted by agriculture, and second because it was cheaper than hand labor and therefore made large fortunes for its owners. For a time, therefore, machinery caused hardship, unemployment and poverty in England because skilled workers lost their jobs when machines could be tended by children. (Many of them, incidentally, migrated to the United States where there was work for all of them.) The designers of English machines also worked more with quality than quantity in mind; American inventors concentrated mainly on the largest possible production and, above all, the greatest possible speed. From the very beginning of the republic the impulse of speed dominated every other. We know now that this speed was necessary if the nation was to hold together; in the early days it seems to have been an unconscious driving force.

There was another reason why what we know as mass production originated in America and only in America. That reason is contained in the Declaration of Independence.

The framers of that remarkable document believed it to be a "self-evident" truth "that all men are created equal." That brings us back to the beginning of this chapter where we found a foreign visitor amazed that, in America, luxuries were commonplace. Throughout our history each American has believed that, in some sense, he is the equal of every other American. He may be less intelligent or, as he is likely to put it, less "smart" than his neighbor. He certainly may be less rich, less lucky or less healthy. But he has rarely believed—as many in other lands still believe—that he has not the *right* to the best of everything. Wealth, power, social importance and high office have always been part of the dream of the individual American. As soon as they can understand words, boys are told that they may one day be President of the United States and all of them believe it.

In the days of the great migrations, the pioneers—though they might have had the humblest origins—dreamed of prosperity ahead. "There's gold," they used to say, "in them thar hills"—and there was. When the first fine machines found their way west, every farmer dreamed of owning a reaper or a thresher, a harvester and, finally, a tractor. When sewing machines came, there was not an American woman in the loneliest farmhouse who did not know that her desire for this luxury could, somehow, be fulfilled. Her granddaughters felt the same way about their refrigerators and toasters and dish-washers.

And when machine production got fairly started, the manufacturers invented new devices to meet those unlimited American desires. One of those which most surprised Europeans was the installment plan, instituted by

Cyrus McCormick and Isaac Singer, by which only a small "down payment" plus a promise was necessary to have farm machinery or a sewing machine delivered to your home. In Europe, the opposite method was in vogue: something was subscribed for in advance and did not become the property of the subscriber until every penny had been paid. Foreigners simply could not understand this trusting of "lower class" strangers.

As soon as manufacturers realized the size of their markets they built faster and more productive machines until, finally, with their enormous sales, they were able to produce much cheaper things. It was this background which made it possible for Henry Ford to install an assembly line which would turn out a finished car every twenty seconds and, after eighteen years of that kind of production, to sell his cars for $300 apiece.

Another important factor in American mass production was the newspaper. In Europe the press existed mainly for the benefit of educated folk able to discuss with intelligence and understanding the affairs of the day. In America, everyone felt entitled to news and politics, so when the penny newspaper was produced it instantly acquired an enormous circulation. The papers not only told of new inventions but they advertised the new products of the factories and every reader felt that he could find a way to buy these things.

Without machines, without the constant new invention and building of machines, without the extraordinary quantity of things they were able to produce, the settlement of our three million square miles of territory would have taken many hundreds of years. Surely, in that time, our nation would have split into many nations with separate customs and hostility among them. This happened in the slow growth of European civilization and, again, in South America to which machines came late. Different groups of migrants would have become widely separated and the national integrity would have been lost. But, as it was, whenever there was a slowing up of the progress, some new invention came along to give it speed: the rapid machine manufacture of axes to cut the forest, fleets of steamboats to carry goods and people up the rivers and across the lakes, machines to cut and process the grain to make it available to everyone, flour mills to grind the wheat in ever-increasing quantity, packing houses for meat, steel for rails for the railroad, locomotives able to move with speed over quick-laid track up steep grades and round sharp curves, the telegraph for constant liaison and, finally, the organization and transmission of electric power.

As we follow the progress across the continent, it is like finding the pieces of a picture puzzle and fitting them together. Usually, pieces on the frontier are hard to fit until we have completed some part of the picture in the rear. Thus the territory acquired in the Mexican War cannot be fitted in until we have pieces representing the gun factories in Hartford, New Haven and Springfield: the great wheat regions of Minnesota and the Dakotas seem to wait for a piece that will show the McCormick reaper plant in Chicago. The discovery of gold deposits in California and Nevada began the demand for the Pittsburgh iron and steel that went into the transcontinental railroads.

As we look back on it the whole process seems continuous, like mass production itself: we seem to see a great assembly line moving from the Atlantic to the Pacific with all the sub-assemblies coming into it at the right places just as, in an automobile plant, the conveyors bearing the engines and the bodies always meet the chassis as it moves along the main line, precisely when they are needed.

It was not, of course, as simple or as smooth as that. There were desperate moments in the building of America when it seemed as if the whole beautiful structure would collapse. Even now, we cannot always feel the security we should like. Yet somehow our ingenuity has usually got us over the crises. It was not an ingenuity we began with; not the famous, legendary "Yankee ingenuity" but an inventiveness we have acquired slowly and under the pressures of terrible necessity.

CHAPTER TWO

"Untouched
by Human Hands"

Driving southwest from the busy industrial
city of Wilmington on the four-lane high-
way of Route 13 to the point where Route 40 branches off to
Baltimore, it is impossible to imagine what this country was
like when Delaware was a Crown Colony. If, however, we
stop at a crossroads just before we come to the Baltimore
pike and drive east we shall find the town of New Castle
preserved almost as it was, with its stately Georgian houses,
its town hall, courthouse, churches and churchyards, for this
place has been protected as a monument to the early history
of which Delaware folk are extremely proud. If, at the same
point on Route 13, we turn west we shall drive along the
Christiana River to where Red Clay Creek empties into it.
On a farm close to this junction, in 1755, was born one of the
first great American inventors. Thirty years later he used the
water of Red Clay Creek to turn a water-wheel and with
the power he thus obtained he operated what was probably
the first continuous, automatic production line in history.

If the ghost of Oliver Evans should come back to this

country along the Delaware River and meet our car on the Christiana road he would not, perhaps, show great surprise. Evans had, in those times which to us seem almost impossibly primitive, a vivid prophetic vision. He understood the forces which would transform the little village of Wilmington that he knew into the tremendous, humming, rhythmic center that it is today, producing not for a state or a nation but for all the world. In his mind's eye, Evans saw great factories with long machine sequences turning out an endless quantity of goods: he saw factory towns joined by railroads before a single locomotive moved in America.

More than a hundred years before an automobile appeared on an American road, Evans was obsessed by the idea that a vehicle carrying its own mechanical power plant was possible and, indeed, in 1805, he actually built such a vehicle and drove it in Philadelphia before an amazed and frightened crowd of spectators. It was a crude affair by the General Motors or Chrysler standards of 1953. It weighed fifteen and a half tons and ran by steam. But it ran. It ran, furthermore, down to the Schuylkill River at which point, when its wheels were removed and a paddle wheel added, it became a motor boat and traveled sixteen miles up the Schuylkill and Delaware rivers and back. So Oliver Evans would also take our modern army amphibious "ducks" in his stride.

This prophetic machine was built in Evans's mature years after much study of steam engines. When he built it, he already had his most useful inventions behind him.

The first of these was worked out during a lull in the tough farm labor he was expected to do when he was twenty-two years old. He had seriously injured his leg mowing grain with a scythe and, for a time, had to give up all physical activity. This gave his mind a chance to move at top speed.

The device Oliver then designed was of no importance to future generations but it was immensely useful at the time and showed the inventor's uncanny grasp of later methods of automatic machine production. It was a machine for making "cards"—hand implements used to comb out raw wool and cotton before spinning it into yarn. These cards were used in pairs and, at first glance, looked something like the curry combs used in grooming horses. To make them by hand was a laborious and painful job. The wire teeth had to be cut and bent and then fastened into rectangular pieces of leather. In 1777 when the war had cut off imported cards, patriotic women and children sat on doorsteps all over the colonies working at them till their fingers bled. Oliver's invention cut and bent the teeth. Later he improved it so that it also pricked the leather and inserted and fixed the bent teeth in it.

At this time, the idea of a single machine doing more than one thing was pure magic. Evans's card-maker performed four successive operations. It even fed the materials into itself so that all the operator had to do was turn a crank. Is it any wonder that the farmers in his family thought, as his father said, that he was "cracked"? Writing of the incident years later (in the third person) Evans's ironic sense of humor appears:

His father's family becoming acquainted with the circumstance, united argument with ridicule, to dissuade him from his visionary schemes. They, not succeeding, gave him up for lost, as a metamorphosis from an industrious man to a whimsical projector. Indeed such little value was attached to his model that even the blacksmith . . . considered it a useless gimcrack . . . and refused to work for him, on such visionary schemes, until George Latimer, Esq., by his persuasive arguments, aided by some good old Jamaica spirits . . . prevailed on him to undertake the job; which succeeded so well, that they all changed their language, and nothing could surpass the ingenuity of Oliver.

The blacksmith's attitude reflects the "low state of the mechanick arts" of the day. The attitude of the provincial governments reflects the prevailing ignorance and skepticism. Evans was unable to get proper protection for his invention. These attitudes did not mean that there were not plenty of people, with no talent themselves, eager to steal another man's idea. Fifteen years later Evans's machine, copied by a Boston manufacturer, was turning out some hundred and fifty thousand cards a year.

From this point on, however, Evans's family was easier to convince. When he left the farm to start a store in Tuckahoe, Maryland, where he would have more leisure for study, his brother Joseph joined him and was, forever after, the partner of his enterprises.

In the store, Oliver and Joseph sold farm implements, kitchen utensils, hardware, lamps, salt, sugar—whatever the farmers could not grow or make. Work in the store was far easier than work on the farm—dictated by weather and animal needs. In the evenings, no longer fatigued by hard physical labor, Oliver could work late at books and drawings. It was then, by the light from shavings burned on a hearth, that he evolved the most important invention of his life and the one with which our story is most concerned. Although he himself had escaped from the farm, his invention proved the greatest boon to American farmers of anything that happened to them in the first half century of the republic's history. Yet in the first ten years it was available to them, they stubbornly refused to recognize its benefits.

Here again, as among the artisans and the mechanics, was a prevailing ignorance—an almost stupid prejudice against anything "new-fangled." Scientific study and agricultural experiment were generally thought to be a waste of time; some farmers even considered them an unholy interference with God's will. However, the farmers' ignorance was, oddly enough, extremely important to the development of the nation. This fact is so significant that it is worth while pausing for a moment, before we look at Oliver Evans's invention, to discover the reason for it.

American farmers in the 1780's were more inclined to leave their farms in God's hands than any others. In Europe, centuries of use, over and over, of the same soil, had taught those who worked it that God favors the man who helps himself by careful practice of economies. Visitors to America were shocked at American farm methods. Livestock was let run in the woods and fields to root out its food, manure was wasted and proper fertilization was almost unknown. What the European did not realize was that Americans, once they had exhausted one patch of land, were able to move on to new acres of virgin soil and plant fields enriched by centuries of rotted leaves or grass. Land sold in those days for a song; it was literally "dirt cheap."

It is well to remember this whenever we read the strange, sometimes incredible, story of America's growth. The reckless farmer, contemptuous of scientific agriculture, kept the frontier moving forever onward. Had he followed the European practice of plowing and planting the same fields that his great-great-grandfather had worked, we should have had little westward movement. The same is true of the use of timber by the pioneer settlers and the builders of the transportation systems which followed them. Today we deplore the destruction of the forests which has resulted in devastating erosion and the consequent loss of millions of tons of our topsoil. Yet if these folk had known better, economizing on lumber, building stone houses, sparing the material of the river rafts and boats and railroad ties, the fuel of the locomotives, how slow would have been their westward progress!

One thing the farmers of the northern colonies grew in good quantity was grain. Oats, corn and wheat were everywhere and wheat spread over many fields in northern Delaware. Wheat being essential to the "staff of life" once it was properly processed, flour mills of a sort could be found wherever it was grown. Always they were on the banks of rivers or streams so that power to turn the millstones could be derived from water wheels.

It was this grinding of wheat into meal and screening the meal into flour which Evans saw all about him and which, in 1782 and '83 as the Revolution came to an end, engrossed all his attention. He had undoubtedly watched the milling since his childhood. It had always fascinated him far more than the job of growing the wheat. Many an afternoon, no doubt, when, as a boy, he got home too late to do the chores, he had stopped for long hours at the Brandywine mills. But now, with his increased mechanical understanding, what he saw moved his imagination along a line which no imagination had ever traveled before.

What he saw he described years later when he wrote his memories of those days. Up the mill's stairs, the millers would carry the grain in sacks on their backs. "All this," Evans wrote, "required strong men." When the grain was ground between the millstones, the meal fell into a trough and "from thence it was with shovels put into the hoist tubs which employed 2 men to attend, one below and one above, and it was emptied in large heaps on the Meal loft, and spread by shovels, and raked with rakes, to dry and cool it . . ." Evans was struck, first, with the amount of human labor used for this operation; second with the waste. Finally, he was shocked by "the great quantity of dirt constantly mixing with the meal from the dirty feet of every one who trampled it, trailing it over the whole Mill." With the acid humor which got into almost everything he wrote, he added that "people did not even then like to eat dirt if they could see it."

When we think of the care that is taken today in food processing to protect every particle even from contact with possibly contaminating air, such an account as this suggests that our ancestors must have been tough indeed. Actually, as we can see from looking at the tombstones in the old graveyards, only the toughest survived and the greater part of most families died in childhood.

It has been said that invention often comes from laziness.

We are told that the automatic valves on steam engines were devised by a boy who was set to open and close the valves on a Newcomen steam pump by hand. No doubt that is what Evans's contemporaries thought of him—that his devices were means of evading proper, industrious manual work. But what good was it to society, to civilization, for men to spend their lives breaking their backs with sacks of grain and rakes and shovels when the river could be made to do this for them and release the men to use their brains instead of their muscles; to go west, perhaps, and help build the nation, to share the fruits of the doctrine that all men are created equal and endowed by their Creator with rights of liberty and the pursuit of happiness? That is what invention did in America. It was not concerned with producing beautiful machines or scientifically perfect processes. Its achievement was the release of men, of needed hands and minds, to the thousand new businesses of making a new nation.

Bit by bit, then, over two years, Oliver Evans worked out not a machine but a sequence of machines, all geared to the same water-wheel, which replaced a sequence—or line—or procession of men. In this scheme, the individual inventions which have proved the greatest boon to mass production were the vertical and horizontal conveyors.

Gravity played a great part in the making of wheat into flour. The grain must first be lifted to the top of a building. From there it fell through devices which cleaned it and regulated its flow to the millstones which ground it. The meal must now be lifted again to the mill's top floor. Being wet with its own juices and hot from the friction of the stones, it must be dried and cooled by spreading it on a floor and raking it. As meal consists of both flour and bran it must be "bolted" or sifted through cloth to separate these. The flour finally reached the ground floor and there it was put in barrels. This double gravity treatment meant continual climbing of stairs.

Evans's conveyor—which forever eliminated the stairs—was an "endless belt" moving over two rollers or pulleys. Everywhere we go today we see endless belts. We see them on escalators in subways and department stores, on production and assembly lines in factories, in the hoisting of bricks, mortar, every kind of material in building. To Evans's vertical belt conveyor or elevator, buckets were attached. As the pulleys were turned by power geared to them from the river the buckets rose continuously. They automatically emptied grain or meal as they turned at the top and descended for more.

The second conveyor was horizontal. It took material from one place to another on the same level. It was a screw or spiral turning in a tube. As it turned it could not help moving grain, meal, or flour along its curves.

The combination of these conveyors kept the grain moving up and across the mill; gravity made it fall between cracking and grinding millstones and through cleaning, cooling and bolting devices until the grain became meal and the meal was turned into "superfine" flour ready to be barreled. One of the inventions of which Evans was most proud was the "hopper boy" named for the unhappy lad who had raked the meal by hand until it was cool and dry. This machine had rakes which, radiating out from a hub turned by the water-wheel did the boy's job by revolving and did it in a far cleaner, more thorough and less wasteful manner.

Every moving part of the mill was geared to the water power. A man emptied the wheat from sacks at one end; another closed the flour barrels and rolled them out at the other. These were the only human beings present. As long as grain was poured into its funnel, the milling was continuous. By 1782, most of the process had been worked out; by 1791 it was complete to the last detail.

The first thing Evans did even before the plans were finished was to build some of the machinery and install it in a mill of his own. Two of his brothers by this time had become sufficiently convinced of his talents to agree to help him provided they were allowed to do farming on the side and also, of course, to share in any profits there might be from the inventions.

By 1787, the mill was running. A few wheat farmers, mainly out of curiosity, brought their grain and saw it turned into flour without human intervention. But what Evans wanted was not to become a miller but to have millers install his machinery for which they would pay him a fee, or let him install it for them. He was able to do this for he had obtained what was called a "monopoly right" from the legislatures of two states, Delaware and Pennsylvania. But he could not persuade the millers.

In 1788, his brother Joseph traveled over a thousand miles and visited over a hundred mills in Delaware, Maryland, Virginia and Pennsylvania, showing Oliver's drawings and model. Every miller shook his head. The methods their

fathers had used were good enough, they said, for them—
and safer. Today, to promote such an invention there would
be photographs of the machinery, advertisements in the
papers and over the radio and television. An agent such as
Joseph Evans would cover ten times the ground in a couple
of weeks. Yet even granting the slowness of this work in
that difficult time, it is hard to understand the stubborn re-
fusal of the millers to accept things which could be of such
benefit to them.

It was in the 1790's that the inventions began to take
hold. By that time the federal patent law had gone through
and Evans had got patents on his machines. One by one,
the Brandywine millers tried them. They did this very
gradually. They put in the machines one at a time. They
would try the elevator for a year before they used the hopper boy. It was well into the new century, before there was
any wide use or even knowledge of the "improvements," as
Evans called them, which carried wheat from the farmer's
sack to the flour merchant's barrel without the intervention
of human labor.

It is true that before his death, the Evans machinery became almost universal in the wheat-growing country in the
East, and mills were springing up behind the westward-
moving frontier. By this time, Evans had added a machine
to pack the flour into barrels so that the entire performance
was automatic. Joseph Evans wrote his brother in some dismay in 1816 after he had traveled a hundred thousand miles
as Oliver's agent:

. . . I find mills in my travels manufacturing flour without
any miller and all done by machinery and shut up . . . I have

walked through these mills calling for the miller and found none and the whole process of grinding, elevating, cooling and Boulting going on and no miller and . . . their neighbors after I had shut up the mill, told me it had become to be a common practice.

Joseph's dismay (which seems to have affected his spelling and punctuation) came from the fact that in these mills Oliver's machinery had been installed without payment of the license—it was stolen, in short. This common behavior of the time resulted in Joseph spending many years of his life on law-suits for patent infringement. But as we read Joseph's letter in the light of the extreme primitiveness of other mechanical progress, we may imagine the eerie impression created by a closed mill working continuously with no one to watch it, while barrels of finished superfine flour rolled out from it!

We may realize how closely the mills followed the westward migration from the fact that in 1837, twelve hundred of them in five western states were turning out two million barrels of flour annually.

A hundred years later, the manufacturer of a breakfast food boasted in his advertisements that it had been made from the raw materials to the final wrapped and sealed package "untouched by human hands." Americans had forgotten by then that the process had been in operation a century before. Now we know that this slogan was really behind the whole movement of American production. It was not always consciously expressed; its ideal was seldom attained. Yet it was an ideal. And in the first decades of the nineteenth century a minimum of human labor was an absolute necessity.

We shall see, in the following chapters, how some twenty or so American geniuses followed in the path that Oliver Evans made and were followed by hundreds of others in producing the greatest quantity of goods and machines with the least number of hands in the quickest time. Evans's followers did not, perhaps, know it but he drew the pattern for one of the principal means by which the United States spread from coast to coast in less than a hundred years.

There was one important factor—apart from the prejudices and ignorances of the farmers—which attached to Evans a suspicion he was never quite able to overcome. When he was seventeen a boy told him of an incident which started him thinking. Several boys, playing round a forge on a rainy afternoon, found an old gun barrel. They filled it with water, stuffed a wad of cloth in one end and held the other in the fire. Presently with a terrific report, the wad shot out of the barrel and hit the wall. The boy who told Oliver was simply amused by this play but it remained in the back of Oliver's mind and kept recurring in his dreams.

He got a gun barrel of his own and experimented. He heated water till steam poured out of the touch-hole in the barrel. He pivoted the barrel and the steam shooting out and hitting a wall caused the barrel to turn at a lively rate.

From that time on Evans's mind moved in the direction of the high-pressure steam engine. Unknown to him several other inventive minds, here and abroad, were moving in the same direction. In one respect, however, Evans's imaginings were unique, at least in America. From the first, he wanted steam to turn the wheels of carriages.

The idea was so fantastic then that, whenever Evans spoke of it, even his friends would try to change the subject. It is probable that this vision worked against him and was responsible for the delay he met in having his other schemes accepted. He included "steam carriages" in his petition to the Pennsylvania legislature for what corresponded in 1786 to a patent for his milling machinery. When the committee came to the part about steam carriages they agreed that the petitioner was insane.

It is certain that a great part of Evans's life was devoted to the automotive effort. He designed many vehicles—some to run on roads, some on rails. In the atmosphere of ignorance which prevailed, one might say that his time was wasted. Only one of his "steam-carriages" ever performed. Yet he did, in that time, build many successful high-pressure steam engines some of which were used for many years after his death. And he also constructed several steam flour mills.

In 1813, sixteen years before the first (imported) locomotive ran in America, Evans wrote:

The time will come when people will travel in stages moved by steam engines, from one city to another, almost as fast as birds fly, fifteen or twenty miles in an hour . . .

A carriage will set out from Washington in the morning, the passengers will breakfast at Baltimore, dine at Philadelphia, and sup at New York, the same day . . . they may . . . travel by night as well as by day; and the passengers will sleep in these stages . . .

He added, showing the bitterness which had accumulated over the years:

And it shall come to pass, that the memory of these sordid and wicked wretches who opposed such improvements, will be execrated, by every good man as they ought to be now.

It is for his work on engines that Evans is chiefly remembered by historians. But it was his continuous, automatic process of turning wheat into flour "untouched by human hands" which was the first true step in the history of mass production in America.

CHAPTER THREE

Spinning and Ginning

WITHIN three years of each other, two mechanical geniuses who influenced the history of the United States to an incalculable extent were born three thousand miles apart. They never met. In the course of their lives, however, they played into each other's hands in a way that could only have happened in young America.

Growing up on a farm in Westborough, Massachusetts, Eli Whitney must soon have become aware of the troubled times into which he had been born. Already in 1765 there were rumblings of discontent through the thirteen British colonies on the Atlantic coast which, ten years later, were to culminate in revolution. Eli was four months past his ninth birthday when the first shots were fired from the smooth-bore "Brown Bess" muskets at Lexington. He was a serious lad, capable of great concentration. He showed little aptitude for farming but he was handy with tools. In the war years both talents were in demand. Eli did the jobs with cows and corn which his father expected of him but his heart was in the manufacture, in very considerable quantities, of iron nails.

Probably few echoes of the American rumblings or of the shots at Lexington and Concord were heard in the mill town of Belper in Derbyshire, England. If they had reached so far, they would no doubt have been drowned by the whirring and clanking of the mill-machinery before they came to the ears of Sam Slater. Sam was close to seven when his red-coated countrymen met the minute-men at Lexington three thousand miles away and the chances are that the incident was not even mentioned in Belper. The Slaters were surrounded by a very different kind of revolution which was bringing both prosperity and misery to England. This was the great Industrial Revolution which, in the 1770's, was getting into its stride: coal, the steam engine, cotton spindles and potters' wheels and ovens were taking men, women and even children from the English farms. These people, especially the children, were suffering from the change: twelve or more hours of factory work a day under hard discipline, confined in ill-ventilated rooms, brought sickness and often death. But the country as a whole was growing rich from the export of the machine-produced textiles and some of the people were benefiting from the cheaper goods.

There was a sharp contrast between England and America at this time. In Britain, it was an age of scientific discovery and important invention. Ever since the brilliant work of Isaac Newton in the first years of the century, waves of excitement over the new scientific and engineering "marvels," as they were called, had swept the country. Great crowds thronged to the opening of canals and other engineering achievements, scientific books were eagerly read, new societies were being formed for the study of "philosophy," as science was called, and even "mechanics," the forerunner of "engineering." Many of the celebrated toolmakers of the nineteenth century—such men as Wilkinson and Bramah—were already at work. Finally, the great machines for the manufacture of cotton and wool had been invented and were being constantly improved.

In America, Benjamin Franklin stood alone as a true scientist. Jefferson was interested in invention but the working out of mechanical devices was, with him, only a hobby. Franklin was deeply respected in America for many of his talents and achievements, but to find appreciation for his work in science, he had to go abroad. Before the American Revolution, the English had accepted him as a disciple of Newton and when, during and after the war, he walked through the streets of Paris, it is said that crowds followed him not because of his statesmanship but because they looked with awe upon so great a scientist.

In this country, however, the lack of interest in applied science is evident from the suspicion in which such men as Oliver Evans were held when they experimented with the steam engine that, at the very moment, was causing excitement all over England. Yet here and there things had happened which pointed vaguely to our industrial future. Bog iron in New England had been smelted and worked in rolling mills, fine hats were made in a Connecticut center, kitchen utensils, glass, furniture, other common articles had been produced. Even this small-scale manufacture had alarmed the English. Wise Englishmen knew well enough that most of the people of the American colonies were also Englishmen; that they had the same native talents, the same enterprise, the same energy as Englishmen in England. What was to prevent these colonial Englishmen from catching the fever from the mother country—the fever of the Industrial Revolution? If that happened, the whole colonial system would collapse. As we have seen, the purpose of a colony was to supply the mother nation with three things: food, raw materials and a market for manufactured goods. As soon as American Englishmen learned how, they would make their own tools, shoes, hardware and, worst of all, cotton and woolen cloth which was the basis of the new prosperity in England.

The first acts of Parliament forbidding any manufactures in the colonies had been ignored in many places. When the great textile machines were invented, Parliament passed laws forbidding the exportation of any machine parts or any plan or model of a machine out of England. Fearing that workmen from the new English factories where these machines were operating might emigrate to America and teach Americans to copy them, Parliament forbade any artisan or workman trained in textile production to travel away from England.

When the War of Independence was over and Britain had forever lost her North American colonies and, therefore, the power to prevent manufacturing in America, she enforced the other laws with increased vigor. At every English port, ships were ransacked for contraband; many a carefully disguised box of machine parts was seized, suspicious passengers were put ashore and severe fines and jail sentences imposed on the smugglers. And the British then, as we have seen, dumped their own manufactures in America at prices below cost to recapture the lost markets. This attempt came so near success that just as Eli Whitney was coming of age the infant United States was in grave danger of again becoming a colony in fact if not in name. Oddly enough, it was an Englishman who played one of the most decisive parts in preventing it.

As Sam Slater grew up on his father's farm in Belper, great things were happening in the town and in other nearby towns. Most of them were the result of the activities of a picturesque character named Richard Arkwright. Arkwright changed the whole pattern of production in the civilized world. He changed the conditions of labor and the relations of labor and capital in England and his system spread all over the continent of Europe and to America. He was the Henry Ford of his day.

Arkwright has been called an inventor; actually he was a combiner and improver, a promoter and user, of the inventions of other men. He began life as a barber in a period when wigs were in fashion. When he cut a man's hair he would save the hair, make wigs out of it and sell them. In this way, he earned enough money—but only just enough —to study "the mechanick arts" in his spare time. In off hours and times when barber business was slack he studied new ways of spinning to replace the slow treadle wheels which represented the furthest advance in this art that the world had made by the mid-eighteenth century.

It is one of the most curious facts in the history of invention that this basic process necessary to clothing should have remained so primitive so long. Weaving, on the other hand, which made thread or yarn into cloth—once it had been spun—had been done for centuries on good machines. Yet weaving was a more elaborate process than spinning. On a loom, a set of parallel threads was strung lengthwise. A device lifted half of these threads—every other thread—while the other half remained in place. Between the lifted threads and the stationary threads an implement called a shuttle was passed. Then the threads which had remained stationary were raised and the shuttle passed back. The shuttle carried a spool so that, as it moved, it left a thread behind it running crosswise or at right angles to the lengthwise threads and in and out between them. The lengthwise threads were called the "warp"; the shuttle thread was the "woof" or the "weft."

In making cloth, it was the warp which, as the loom moved, took the worst beating. With the constant raising and lowering, these threads would wear and break, whereas the weft on which there was little strain remained intact. None of the cotton yarn which the old-fashioned wheels had spun was strong enough for warp. It was necessary, therefore, to use linen thread for the warp and this made cotton cloth costly.

In 1764, an inventor named James Hargreaves had thought up a revolutionary machine called a "spinning Jenny" which made the spinning wheel obsolete and was, in principle, the basis of all spinning machinery forever after. Hargreaves had happened on his idea accidentally. One day, while he was watching his wife spin, the wheel tipped over. It continued to revolve but, being on its side on the floor, the spindle was in a vertical instead of a horizontal position. It instantly occurred to the inventor that a large number of vertical spindles ranged side by side could be turned by the same wheel and that, therefore, many threads could be spun at once. He named his machine "Jenny" after his wife who had caused this highly productive accident.

The Hargreaves jenny was a more basic and original invention than any Arkwright ever made. Nevertheless, even it—though it could spin a hundred threads at a time—could not make cotton thread that was tough enough for warp. That was Arkwright's contribution. By adding rollers, he was able to strengthen the thread and make it of even thickness: when this was done it could go on the loom as warp and the whole business of the manufacture of cotton cloth was revolutionized. Arkwright called his invention a "water frame" because, whereas the jennies had been operated by hand, this one could be moved by a water-wheel.

Other inventions came thick and fast in these years of scientific awakening when England was taking on new life. There were carding machines to prepare the cotton wool for spinning, replacing the old hand cards we encountered in the youth of Oliver Evans. Looms were given new speed by a device known as the "flying shuttle." Arkwright experimented with these machines and improved some of them; he combined them in sequences and set them up in new institutions known as "factories."

Although these brilliant inventions were made in those exciting years, the inventors often had an exceedingly difficult time. Along with the wave of intense interest, among intelligent observers, of the new "wonders of science," came a wave of fear which spread rapidly among the workers. These people, seeing the new machines which produced so fast and needed so little skill to operate, thought they saw resulting unemployment for themselves. They were wrong as we now know for the machines increased production to such an extent that there were, eventually, jobs for everyone, but the workers of the 1760's and 70's could not believe it. They formed mobs, therefore, rioted and smashed every machine they could find. The result was that the inventors had to work in secret and some of them were impoverished by the loss of their materials and labor.

In America, these destructive mobs rarely gathered. The reason for this was that when machines were used in America their use was forced by a shortage of labor whereas in England they were invented in an age of scientific awakening and imposed upon a society in which there was already a labor surplus.

One who suffered most from the anger of the mobs was Arkwright. It is said that he became so poor that he was ashamed, because of the raggedness of his clothes, to be seen in public. He was, however, a person of persistence and determination. He left the town where the riots had occurred and, in Nottingham, went to call on a wealthy stocking manufacturer named Jedediah Strutt. The meeting of Strutt and Arkwright was the first step in the strange sequence which ended with the foundation of the textile industry in

America, and with it the Industrial Revolution jumped across the Atlantic.

Arkwright explained to Jedediah Strutt the plans which had been maturing in his mind for the new "factory system." Industry at that time in England was what was known as "domestic." A great part of the country's manufactures was carried on in the homes of the workers. This was true of the entire textile industry. The capitalist employer would "farm out" his raw cotton or wool to many workers who owned their own machines and the whole family would work at it. When the spinning and weaving were finished, the cloth was returned to the employer for sale by him. Sometimes the employer rented machines to the workers. To the artisans there were certain advantages to this system. They could set their own hours for work. They did not have to leave home. Whole families could work together. It had, however, certain drawbacks for the employer. It was difficult to deliver and collect the goods and to discipline the workers, keep them in order and on the job. It was Arkwright's plan to abolish all this. He wanted to set up machines in a building, arranged in a proper sequence, and all geared to a "prime mover"—a power source such as a waterwheel or, later, a steam engine. He believed the workers should assemble at the machines at a certain hour and remain until a certain hour. They should follow a set of strict rules—as in an army. (In some of the factories, after the system got started, they were not even allowed to talk during work hours.) They could no longer work in family groups. For certain machines men operatives were wanted, for others women; for still others, where little strength was needed, children sufficed.

Arkwright convinced Strutt that the time had come when the old domestic scheme was no longer good enough. For one thing machines were going to be too large in the future to be housed in cottages. Also the efficiency which came from having a whole process under one roof would bring enormously increased production. Strutt therefore entered into a partnership with Arkwright, erected buildings and let Arkwright equip them. He established a mill at Nottingham, one at Milford and, finally, one at Belper where the Slaters lived.

When Strutt built in Belper (in 1775) William Slater, father of Sam, arranged for him the purchase of a particularly choice piece of land with a swift stream running through it to turn his mill. Thus Jedediah Strutt and William Slater became close friends and seven-year-old Sam found a new interest in watching the building and furnishing of the mill. For seven years the boy found his greatest pleasure in the magnificent new Arkwright machinery and, at fourteen, he was ready to dedicate his life to this interest.

In 1783, Sam bound himself for a six-year apprenticeship to Jedediah Strutt. His father was then dead and Sam was on his own. He was a self-reliant boy, old for his years, tireless in any work which had captured his imagination.

This was the year the War of Independence came to an end in America. A new nation had emerged from the long struggle—a nation which was tired, disorganized and uncertain of its direction but which, after all, was free.

As Washington's ragged and hungry armies were demobilized, the country was in the grip of a demoralizing depression. The people were heavily in debt as a result of buying on credit or with a currency which had little or no value. New England, its sea trade stopped by the war, suffered especially. Massachusetts farmers, led by an agitator named Daniel Shays, attempted an armed rebellion. Some of the new states which, as colonies, had united against a common enemy, were, now that the war was over, hostile to one another.

It was in these distressed times that Eli Whitney became an adult. His ambition was to go to college: his farmer father wanted him to become a lawyer. As the war ended he gave up his nail-making enterprise and taught school until at twenty-three he had saved enough to enter Yale. As a freshman he was far beyond the age of his classmates. It is remarkable, when we remember this man's extraordinary genius, to realize how late his education and his start in life arrived.

While Whitney was in college, devoting himself, not to those studies which would lead to his later triumphant achievements, but to the law, things of immense importance were happening elsewhere. In 1789, Whitney's freshman year, the Constitution of the United States was ratified. This drew the new states into a new entity: from the loose sort of league of nations they had formed before there was now the basis for a close-knit, solid union. In spite of this advance, however, several patriotic Americans—Alexander Hamilton among them—were greatly worried lest, by remaining farmers, the people should lose the means of prosperity and wealth offered by the natural resources of the country to manufacturing industries.

These patriots were not unaware of what was happening in England. Franklin and others had told of the Industrial Revolution with its new power and machinery. Stories of the Arkwright mills had drifted across the ocean ever since the war. In Pennsylvania, Massachusetts and Rhode Island, special attention was given to modern methods of spinning cotton. Prizes were offered to anyone who could make any machine which would compare with those which were now turning out countless yards of fine cloth in England—much of which had been sold in America.

A persistent worker in this direction was a Rhode Island Quaker named Moses Brown of the firm of Almy and Brown in Pawtucket. He had built machine after machine for cotton spinning by water power but all without success. The devices made for him by the best mechanics he could find would run for a while and then break down. The machines cost him and his partner more for repairs than they brought in profits for the year. The reason was, of course, that the mechanics had no plans or specifications to work from and only parts of English machines which had been smuggled into the country, and not enough ingenuity to make original inventions. Britain, in short, was accomplishing precisely what she had set out to do—making the new nation wholly dependent upon British industry.

This was the condition, then, when Sam Slater in Belper finished the term of his apprenticeship with Jedediah Strutt and began to take an active part in the management of the machinery which Arkwright had installed in the Strutt mill.

In 1789—the year Whitney entered Yale—Sam was twenty-one, complete master of machine spinning, bursting with energy, on fire with ambition and, in the mill-town of Belper which had come to seem confining to him, exceedingly restless.

Strutt had settled into a comfortable middle age. He was prosperous, content to let his business go on making a decent income for his heirs. Arkwright had moved on to establish his factory system all over England. One day Sam frankly asked his boss about the possibilities of his future. Strutt answered that there would be plenty of security in the business of producing cotton. The industry was established, steam engines had replaced water power, no particular enterprise or originality would be necessary. It would simply go on and on.

For Sam, this was not enough. He wanted not security but adventure. He wanted to strike out for himself, take his chances and hope to start some new, expanding work free from traditional restraint. At home he knew that advance would be slow. When he reached Strutt's age he would probably become another Strutt, sedentary, complacent, content to raise a family and pass the business on to his sons.

For several years, Sam had been hearing about the new nation across the Atlantic. He listened eagerly to stories of its freedom, its endless opportunity. Occasionally he would find a copy of an American newspaper and read it through. Slowly the desire had grown in him to see this land for himself and try, there, to make a new start, using his valuable experience in the Strutt-Arkwright mill. One day, he came on the report, in a Philadelphia newspaper, of a hundred-pound reward paid by the Pennsylvania Society for the Encouragement of Manufactures and the Useful Arts for building a carding machine. From then on, his plans matured.

The first need was secrecy. He was one of those people whose emigration was specifically prohibited by Act of Parliament. At first it seemed to him that if he were going to construct machines in America, he must be able to smuggle some sort of plan, some model, some list of dimensions with him. Then, suddenly, he realized that this was not necessary.

Sam Slater had the rare gift of a photographic memory. Over the years, the Arkwright machines which he had watched and worked so constantly had become engraved upon his mind in every detail. He could recite the size of every part of every machine in inches and fractions of an inch as perfectly as an actor recites his part in a play.

In farmer's clothes, he engaged passage on a ship. He practiced the speech and manner of a rustic. He took with him only a few clothes and possessions which he readily displayed to the inspectors. He took not a single sketch or memorandum.

He landed in New York almost penniless. He got a temporary job in a so-called "manufactory" in which were a few imperfect textile machines. In the evenings he would walk along the water front. One night he got in conversation with a captain whose ship plied between New York and Providence, Rhode Island. To this sympathetic person Sam confided his hopes, told his experience and showed a

confidence in his ability which induced the captain to tell
him of the tribulations of Moses Brown in Pawtucket and
to offer to take a letter from Sam to Brown. On the tenth
of December, 1789, the Quaker wrote his answer and sent
it back to Sam in New York.

We are destitute [he wrote] of a person acquainted with water-
frame spinning. . . . As the frame we have is the first attempt
of the kind that has been made in America, it is too imperfect
to afford much encouragement. . . . If thy present situation does
not come up to what thou wishest, and, from thy knowledge of
the business, can be ascertained of the advantages of the mills,
so as to induce thee to come and work ours, and have the *credit*
as well as advantage of perfecting the first water-mill in America,
we should be glad to engage thy care. . . .

We may imagine the effect of such a letter upon a poor
and lonely young man whose insistent ambition was precisely what Brown had described—of perfecting the first
mill of its kind in the new world until it achieved the success that Arkwright's establishments had attained in the old!

When, however, a few weeks later, he went with Moses
Brown and his partner to their mill in Pawtucket, he saw
at once that what was needed was not "perfecting" but
building anew from the ground up.

"These will not do," he said after one look at the machines. "They are good for nothing in their present condition, nor can they be made to answer."

He agreed then to undertake the new construction with
certain provisions. First, he must be given a first rate mechanic to assist him. Second, that mechanic must be put
under bond of secrecy. Finally, Slater asked for a fifty per

cent share of all the profits which his new machinery would earn. These provisions showed that Sam was an astute businessman, as well as a skilled artisan. We may, at first, be surprised that he had no compunction about copying Arkwright's machines; that his only scruple was for his own protection lest the secrets become known outside the business to which he had attached himself. It must be remembered, however, that Arkwright in his turn had appropriated the inventions of others and that his patents were, at the moment, in dispute in England. By 1790, indeed, the textile machinery was in great part public property in Great Britain and Arkwright's success had come not through control of patents but through what we call "know-how."

As his confidential assistant, Slater engaged Sylvanus Brown, of the widespread Brown family of Rhode Island, one of the rare expert mechanics of the period who was later distinguished in another field. It is striking how so many of the people of this story of early industry in America keep turning up in other branches. The reason for this is that America's industrial revolution started from a small group to which most later activity can be traced. Sylvanus Brown and his son became pioneers in the machine-tool development which eventually placed New England on one of the world's highest industrial levels.

For a year, Slater carried on the design of the machinery in Brown's workshop. Sam would make working drawings from memory on the timbers of the building and Brown would execute them in wood and metal. Only once in his work did he get stuck; that was in the making of a carding machine and Brown is said to have got him over that hurdle.

They were assisted by a ten-year-old boy and a Negro who, during the experiments before the machines were ready to hitch to the water wheel, furnished their motive power with the muscles of his arms and back.

Before the end of 1791, Slater had reproduced the Belper mill entire; it was moving by water power and spinning more yarn than Almy and Brown had ever imagined possible. In another three years, the Slater mills had spun so fast that the raw cotton gave out and they had to shut down.

At this point, there occurred in the state of Georgia an event which altered the whole history of the South. It was one of those astonishing coincidences which mark so much of our early history. It answered the prayers of Almy, Brown and Slater. It also made the everlasting reputation of the other hero of our story.

When Eli Whitney graduated from Yale he was offered a job tutoring some boys in the interior of the state of Georgia. His aim was still the law. The job, he guessed, would not be too exacting; he would live comfortably and be able to study for the bar in his spare time.

The journey by ship being a long one Eli developed a pleasant friendship with two shipmates, Mrs. Nathanael Greene who owned a plantation near Savannah and Phineas Miller, her plantation manager. The result was that, on landing, Eli stayed for a time on the Greene plantation before pushing on to his tutoring job.

At that time cotton grew wild over much of the state of Georgia. The cotton gave promise of infinite wealth but the promise was defeated as soon as it was picked. The fibers clung so tenaciously to the green seeds that a Negro slave working all day could only clean a single pound.

The planters who stopped at the Greene plantation kept voicing their despair over this enormous potential wealth which surrounded them and saying that if only someone could devise a machine to replace the slaves' slow fingers untold fortunes could be realized. Eli, hearing these things and being a far greater mechanic than he would ever be a lawyer, soon produced his celebrated "cotton gin" which multiplied the daily amount of cleaned cotton by fifty.

It was a simple device, employing teeth on a wheel which drew the cotton through slits so narrow that the seeds could not follow.

Whitney got a patent on his invention and he formed a partnership with Mrs. Greene's manager, Phineas Miller, to manufacture the gins. Abandoning his tutoring job for this new venture, he went to New Haven and established a workshop there where, financed by Miller, he expected to turn out gins rapidly enough to satisfy the southern demands. It was then that, like so many of our early mechanical heroes, he discovered there was almost no one who knew enough to help him with the simplest elements of machine construction.

The southern planters could not wait. When we realize the gigantic need for this machine and the temptation of the fabulous wealth it promised we can understand them. The United States patent law was then only three years old and was impossible to enforce on remote Georgia plantations. The result was that variations of Whitney's gin were made all over the state with no money or credit given to

him. The cotton plant which before had been let run wild
was now carefully cultivated on a large scale. Presently it
was grown in all the gulf states. Its wildfire spread gave
new impetus to slavery and thus the cotton gin became a
factor more than fifty years later in the causes of the Civil
War.

In a single year after Eli Whitney's invention, the United
States cotton crop increased from five to eight million
pounds. Six years later (1800) thirty-five million pounds
were produced. In 1805 this figure doubled, rising to seventy
million; in 1820 it went up to 160,000,000 and in 1825, the
year of Whitney's death, it was 225,000,000 pounds.

It is easy to see, therefore, how the worries of Sam Slater
were set at rest. As the new shiploads of cotton arrived at
the Providence docks, he was able to expand his mills and
to build others. He became a wealthy industrialist and was
rightly called the "father of the American textile industry."
Through his efforts the United States was first freed from
dependence on Great Britain. Cloth from the Rhode Island
mills and the Massachusetts ones which followed them
went out to the new towns behind the frontier and helped
bring civilization to the wilderness. The American industrial revolution, which arrived early in the nineteenth century, unquestionably got a large part of its impetus from
the cotton which Whitney and Slater gave us.

We must return now to pick up the thread of Eli Whitney's career. The effort to maintain his patent and the
temporary misfortune of its final loss led him into the
greatest single invention in the history of mass production.

CHAPTER FOUR

Machines
to Make Machines

Eli whitney's belief that he could make machines in New Haven for sale and use in Georgia shows how far ahead of his time his thinking was. Today, automobiles for the whole world are made in Detroit. Most of the nation's electric light bulbs come out of Corning and Schenectady in New York State; its plate and window glass are made in Pittsburgh. But in the 1790's, when Whitney came back from Georgia full of hope for his invention and set up his little workshop in New Haven, such things were out of reach of the American imagination.

In that time what manufacturing there was found only local markets. A grist-mill ground for the immediate community, a saw-mill sawed boards for houses that were built within a few miles of it, shoemakers, carpenters, blacksmiths, gunsmiths, potters, tailors, tanners, harness-makers had their customers in the village in which they lived or in a small district or borough of a city. The exceptions to this were a few goods which were made in seaports—lumber, preserved fish, tar, rum—which could be shipped on long, slow sea voyages.

One reason for this was that transportation was so primitive. Except along the coast there were no roads worthy of the name. Even those from New York to Philadelphia and Baltimore were impassable to wheeled vehicles at certain seasons and, a few years later when the national capital was established on the edge of a Potomac swamp, President John Adams got stuck traveling from his Massachusetts home to the new Washington. Westward travel was, in those days, mainly by river boats and pack horse, though in a snowy winter long treks were made by sledge and sleigh.

The second reason—and one with which Whitney was especially concerned—was that nearly all the manufacture of the day was by handicraft. The difference between handicraft and industrial methods is a vital one and must be understood before any grasp of this American adventure in mass production is possible. It was not, in the beginning, merely a difference between hand and machine work. In handicraft, each workman completed an entire article by himself. By the industrial system, an article was divided into the parts which composed it and the making of each part was given to one man as his exclusive job. When machinery took over, then, it was only necessary for each machine to perform one small operation.

In following this Whitney story we must bear in mind the fever of excitement which, in Georgia, followed the news of the miracles the gin could perform. When a man sees himself surrounded by endless wealth which has suddenly become available to him he is in no mood to wait six months or a year until a sailing vessel brings from far away Connecticut the means to that wealth. He wants it now, tomorrow, before someone else takes it away from him. His friend on a neighboring plantation may have been lucky enough to secure one of the genuine Whitney gins and, with the labor of one man, is turning out a hundredweight of cleaned cotton a day while he has to watch a dozen slaves struggle to free from its seeds less than a quarter that amount with their fingers! The temptation to tell his carpenter to look through his neighbor's window some moonlight night, make a sketch of the machine and then come home and build one like it, was irresistible. By the time the law, moving slowly by ship and horse from Washington, reached our planter to sue him for the infringement of a patent, he would have made money enough to hire a good lawyer for a defense which might last for years, or, if necessary, to pay his fines.

Whitney may or may not have realized all this natural impatience. What he did know was that there were not enough good carpenters and metal workers in Georgia who could be assembled in one place to manufacture his machines in sufficient quantity to supply the demand, whereas in New Haven, a compact city with, as he remembered, a a good population of artisans, the work could be done fast and continuously enough to compensate for the time needed to ship the finished gins south. Whitney also had faith in the power of the new federal government to protect him. Finally, he knew he would feel more at home, with more energy to work, among people whose ways he knew and

understood than in the strange, exotic and lazy atmosphere
of the deep South.

He was doomed to a succession of disappointments. When
he had set up shop he found the greatest difficulty in getting
skilled assistants. Even in the short time since he had left
college hundreds of artisans of all kinds had gone west. Carpenters, metal-workers, forgemen, wheelwrights had been
caught up in the mad rush out to the empty land as if its
vacuum had drawn them. The few helpers he was able to
get were clumsy, made mistakes and needed constant watching. Then even some of those began to drop out and Eli
found that they too had joined the migration. Finally, it
began to look as if he would have to depend on boys of
twelve or fourteen and, if this happened, he would have to
find some way to eliminate the need for skill in the making
of his gins for, clever as these lads might be, they could not
have the experience of a mature worker. It was then, apparently, that he became fully convinced that a system of work
wholly different from the handicraft one would be necessary to avoid rapid and total failure.

Assuming that, under the handicraft system, it would take
a man three days to make a gin, beginning with the box,
then making the drum, then putting the teeth or saws into
the drum, then working out the slots through which the
saws would pass and so on until everything had been fitted
together, it would then be true that six men in three days
could make six gins. Each of the six would be a little different from every other, depending on the art or skill of the
individual craftsman.

Under the industrial system, the gin would be divided into six parts and the making of each part would be given to one man as his exclusive job. Thus one man would make only the box or housing, another the axle and crank, another the saw drum, another the saws, and a fifth the slots. The sixth man would put all these parts together, picking them up from the piles in front of each workman as he walked round the shop. With this system each worker would need only one simple, specialized skill and by performing a single operation over and over would soon become highly practiced in it.

Unfortunately we have few records of the details of Whitney's work during those early days in New Haven but we have enough to know that this system in some form was tried and that it made the work go faster. But we know positively from the records of his later almost incredible achievement that, during all this time, he must have been slowly, methodically working out the plan of his later success.

After dividing up the work, although this undoubtedly increased the number of gins which could be made in a given number of days, Whitney still could not have been satisfied. Although he had given each workman a pattern to follow, the parts when they were ready for assembly varied and sometimes they would not fit together without extra cutting or filing. An axle would be too large for its bearings or the saw teeth might be crooked on the drum and so prevent its turning. Evidently, therefore, the new system had not yet fully compensated for the loss of skill and something must be done to balance the clumsiness of the boys and unskilled men he had been obliged to hire in place of real craftsmen. *The manufacture, in short, must be made fool-proof.*

With the succession of misfortunes which dogged Whitney as he tried to keep up with the insatiable demand for cotton gins, he was not able to do much to give his thoughts solid form in the kind of tools he knew he must have. Storms beset the ships on which the gins were shipped, his workers and he himself went through intervals of sickness, the money Miller was able to send was pitifully inadequate and, finally, on a cold night in March, his shop burned to the ground destroying his lathe, his workbenches, his tools, his patterns, all his papers and the gins which were being built at the time.

Whitney rebuilt everything and made improvements in the shop. For a time his optimism was undefeated. Gradually, however, he knew he was beaten. Through 1796 and 97, suits against infringers of his patent were costly and unsuccessful. In October, 1797, he wrote his partner:

The extreme embarrassments which have been a long time accumulating upon me, are now become so great, that it will be impossible for me to struggle against them many days longer. It has required my utmost exertions to *exist,* without making the least progress in our business. I have labored hard against the strong current of disappointment, which has been threatening to carry us down the cataract, but I have labored with a shattered oar and struggled in vain. . . .

Whitney's tragic impasse was fortunate for the future history of the United States. It is obvious enough to us that the kind of local handicraft tradition Whitney was struggling against could never have made possible the tremendous expansion of the country and held it together as a single nation at the same time. The old idea of the subsistence farm as a self-sufficient unit—with the farmer who was a jack-of-all-trades and in the winter made his furniture, shoes, implements and utensils—was far too slow and too isolated. The shoemaker or blacksmith who plied his trade in a New England village could only supply a few neighbors, not a vast moving horde clearing countless acres of forest and swarming over the prairie. No, goods must be made in quantity at the places in which it was most convenient to make them: by a river for power or transport, or near a source of raw materials. Then new means of transportation must be as quickly created to carry them to the moving markets.

Actually Whitney's next move after the defeat of the cotton gin did not directly furnish the frontier but it established a pattern from which all the demands of future frontiers could be supplied. He made it, boldly, with astonishing self-confidence (considering the beating he had just taken) in the spring of 1798.

It is usually supposed, by those who have not been too thorough in their reading of American history, that the United States and France have always been friends. For the most part, this is true. In 1798, however, the year in which Whitney decided to abandon the cotton gin for a more lucrative adventure, the two nations came perilously close to war and that conflict was avoided only because of the wisdom and patience of the men who then controlled the American government.

The France which had sent Lafayette and an army to help us to independence had been torn apart by the French Revolution. That Revolution had at first had many American sympathizers—Thomas Jefferson among them—but their sympathy had been cooled by the insults with which the new French government had greeted our envoy and especially by the plunder by French privateers of some three hundred American vessels in the Caribbean. The fact that the attacks on the ships were said by the French to be in the interest of France's war with England made little difference to Americans. The American government ordered immediate preparations for defense which included a dozen warships and muskets enough to equip an army, all to be made with utmost speed.

To Whitney, looking about for some new manufacture to replace the unprofitable cotton gin, the news of the need of muskets came like a breath of fresh air. Muskets, the more he thought about it, would really prove the new system which must, by then, have pretty fully matured in his mind. Furthermore the deal would not be with individuals of dubious credit, it would be with the government of the United States which could not repudiate its debts. Also, only a government was rich enough to order this kind of mechanism in large enough quantity to test the new theory.

On the first of May, therefore, he wrote this extraordinary letter to the Secretary of the Treasury:

By the debates in Congress I observe that they are about making preparations for procuring arms, etc., for the United States.

... I should like to undertake to manufacture ten or fifteen thousand stand of arms.

I am persuaded that machinery moved by water, adapted to this business, would greatly diminish the labor and facilitate the manufacture of this article. Machines for forging, rolling, floating, boreing, grinding, polishing, etc., may all be made use of to advantage. . . .

He explained that as this was probably not the business of the Treasury, he would be obliged if the gentleman would pass the letter on to the Secretary of War. His reason for this roundabout procedure was that the Treasury's secretary was Oliver Wolcott, a personal friend and admirer, and this assured him that the message would not go into the waste basket.

For one man to undertake such an order at a time when all the government's armories working together at top speed could not have turned out such a quantity within any reasonable time must have seemed highly visionary to anyone who knew gun-making procedure. Obviously it would require the services of hundreds of trained gunsmiths working full time. A gunsmith in those days was called an "artist" and it was a good designation. Even a smooth-bore musket was a work of art almost like a painting or a piece of sculpture. Collectors treasure the military flintlocks and the long-barreled Kentucky rifles of the period much as connoisseurs of furniture value the chairs by Duncan Phyfe or banjo clocks. They were made entirely by hand with tender care and each piece was slightly different from every other so that experts could spot the maker by some characteristic tool mark on the stock or lock. Some of these gunsmiths were famous. They were few and far between and greatly in demand.

On the face of it, therefore, Whitney's boast was impossible. Yet his cotton gin—stolen as it had been—had given him a high reputation in the government. Thomas Jefferson himself had helped him get his patent. Congressmen such as Goodrich of Connecticut, cabinet members such as Wolcott, had learned of the new prosperity his invention had brought to the South and they had watched his tribulations in New Haven with sympathy. Important men in New Haven were ready to swear to his integrity and his talents. Perhaps, also, the officials who received his offer were not fully aware of the technical difficulties the filling of this order presented.

Whatever these were, Wolcott thought, Eli Whitney would never have made the offer unless he had been certain he could come through. Within six weeks, therefore, a contract was signed and sealed whereby Whitney agreed to deliver ten thousand smooth-bore, flintlock muskets complete with bayonet, powder horn and cartridge box to the government of the United States within two years.

Wolcott was right in his estimate of Whitney. Eli would certainly never have made such a proposition as this had he not thought the whole performance through, carefully, methodically, with countless sheets of paper covered with figures and diagrams and, probably, whittled models illustrating various stages of the work. He had thought this out during the dark hours of his discouragement over the cotton gin; at night in his workshop when the men and boys had left; pacing up and down in the shadows of his half-finished machines cast by a flickering tallow candle. He did not realize it but the picture he evolved in those lonely hours was of an entirely new era in the world.

He was not a gunsmith. He had no intention whatever of hiring gunsmiths. He had no interest in gunsmiths. He was an inventor, a manufacturer, an engineer—though the word was not used in 1798. Today a mechanical engineer knows that he can set up machinery to make anything—rifles, airplanes, telephone receivers, sewing machines or electric fans. He need not be an expert on any particular gadget or mechanism. Once he gets, from an expert—an inventor, say—a set of drawings of the parts of a gun or bicycle or clock with notes as to how they fit together, he can set up a factory with machines to make those parts and, presently, out of the factory pour guns, bicycles or clocks boxed and ready for the markets. We all know how easily nowadays a factory which makes bedsprings or women's compacts can be converted to munitions manufacture. Whitney had been making cotton gins. He now decided to make smooth-bore flintlock muskets and, with his decision, the "artist" gunsmith began to fade forever out of the world picture.

Watching clumsy workmen fumble the parts of a cotton gin, Whitney quickly realized that, somehow, he must put his own skill into every hand. He must eliminate guesswork "by eye" entirely. He did this by "jigs." A jig is a guide for a tool so that the tool no longer has to depend on a shaky hand or imperfect vision. A ruler is a simple jig: with it you can draw a straight line almost without looking at it.

Whitney made gadgets which held a tool against a piece of wood (called the "work") that was being turned in a lathe. He made automatic stops which would disconnect work from tool at the precise instant when the cut was deep enough or a diameter correct. He used sheets of metal in which holes correctly spaced had already been drilled as guides to get correct spacing in piece after piece of drilled work. He made clamps to hold things tightly on his bench in a correct position while guided chisels or milling wheels cut at them. With enough of these jigs, a worker simply could not go wrong; he could even look out the window as he worked.

It is surprising when we see today's precision of machine tools wholly actuated by jigs and fixtures to realize that these *did not exist* in America until Whitney made them. Actually they did not exist in any quantity or variety anywhere in the world in 1798. A mechanic's only rule was the "rule of thumb." No wonder the muskets differed!

Whitney knew that the speed of manufacture would multiply once *identical* parts could be made. The human eye and hand could never produce two things exactly alike. A machine, however, properly equipped with jigs could turn out any number without a hairsbreadth variation among them. So you could have the parts of your musket—trigger, lockplate, frizzen, etc.—in separate piles, pick one of each at random from each pile and because machines had made them all true they would fit together into a complete firearm!

His plan was to divide his factory, or "mill" as he called it, into departments—one for barrels, one for stocks, one for each lock piece—and equip every department with proper machines. The parts as they came off the machines could be gathered up, taken to an assembly room and put together. Filing, fitting, making over, adjusting—all the fussy, tedious gunsmith's work would be eliminated. All these departments could work at the same time so that the entire manufacture would be continuous, uninterrupted. The halts of the old method as, for example, when a gunsmith finished his musket, looked at it, admired it, put it on a shelf, rested awhile and then sorted out his tools to begin again, carving the stock on a new one—all these time-consuming stops and starts would be ended forever. The machines would be belted to a shaft turned by a water-wheel and the whole mill would hum rhythmically with the rapid, unceasing work.

Unfortunately Whitney had again reckoned without the "low state of the mechanick arts." By inventing machines to make the gun parts he had eliminated the need for skill in operating them. But how about making these machines in the first place? They were brand new devices. Drills, milling machines, the machines he had described in his letter to Wolcott for "forging, rolling, floating, boreing, grinding, polishing, etc."—these had to be made slowly, experimentally, by hand. Whitney could find no one skillful enough to make them. He had to make them himself and, in certain cases, he even had to make his own tools.

We can get some idea of what Whitney was up against from the fact that when Henry Ford abandoned his Model T it took him a year to tool a factory to make Model A.

What Whitney was doing was "tooling," though he did not call it that—it would be a century and a quarter before that verb would come into existence. He was "tooling" a factory for mass production for the first time. It was a crude sort of mass production, sure enough. There were no assembly lines. There were no "tolerances" of a ten or hundred thousandth of an inch. Yet it was the mass production pattern all the same: the Whitney mill on Mill River, Connecticut, was the archetype of the Ford plant on the River Rouge.

When the time came for Whitney to deliver the first four thousand muskets, he had only five hundred. The War Department officials were disturbed and suspicious. Whitney could not make them understand that although there were only five hundred muskets ready, his plant was "tooled" for ten thousand; that the tooling was the hardest part and that now the muskets could "pour out" of the machines. There were no words to explain these things in 1798. It was all entirely new.

To convince the skeptics, he had to put on a demonstration. He had to travel to the new city of Washington to which the national capital had just moved. He took with him ten disassembled muskets. He showed a group of high-powered officials (including some army "brass"), that picking pieces *at random,* muskets could be assembled virtually *without tools.* From what we know of it the demonstration was dramatic and exciting—like a magician's show. Even President Adams and Thomas Jefferson were there. They were convinced, Eli was extravagantly praised and the time of his contract extended.

It is doubtful if anyone except perhaps Thomas Jefferson saw behind Whitney's demonstration in Washington anything truly revolutionary in the history of industry. They were impressed by the fact that the interchangeability of the musket parts offered a new military possibility. If in a combat action, a number of muskets should be damaged it would be possible to pick them up, take them apart and assemble some new muskets out of the pieces that remained whole. *This had never been possible before.* Admitting this and admitting that the firearms Whitney showed were nicely made—superior, indeed, even to those which had been imported—their imaginations went no further. It did not occur to them that the system might apply to the making of mechanisms other than muskets.

It took Whitney eight years instead of three to complete the order. During this time the government was exceedingly generous to him, advancing him money so that almost the entire sum of $134,000 reached him before the contract was fulfilled. Here is an instance in which government, apparently so indifferent to other inventors, showed real enthusiasm for an achievement of mechanical ingenuity. In 1812, the War Department was eager to conclude a second agreement—this time for fifteen thousand muskets and from then on a happy ending to this inventor's checkered career of struggle and hard luck was assured. In the course of his life, the speed and efficiency of the system became recognized. Visitors from all over the world came to see the factory at Hamden, Connecticut, where the parts of muskets were made "as like one another as the impressions from a steel engraving" and where machines were used to make machines.

When Whitney died in 1825, the flourishing business passed to his son. The factory became a center from which what was known as "the American system" passed out to hundreds of other manufacturing centers all over the country where it was improved, made faster, more economical and more precise. We shall trace the spread of it as the frontier moved and we shall find how essential it became to the movement.

In our picture puzzle, then, we must put in the piece representing this little New Haven suburb before many of the large western pieces will fit properly. We shall see how everywhere in the new growing factory towns of the east highly productive machines and continuous machine sequences replaced the men that had gone west to carve the great areas of prairie and forest, lake and river that year after year were added to the nation. And, as we go on with the story, it will become increasingly evident that what grew out of Whitney's muskets could have developed nowhere in the world but in the United States.

It is time now to follow some of these pioneers with their axes and hunting rifles, their later ox-carts and covered wagons and flatboats to see what sort of job confronted them in the wild lands which only the feet of animals and Indians had trod.

CHAPTER FIVE

The Woods and the Trees

RIDING incessantly among the first crude settlements of Indiana, Illinois, Missouri and Michigan, preaching the Gospel to any who would halt their work to listen to him, a Baptist missionary named John Mason Peck learned almost all there was to know about the pioneers. With the Bible propped up on the saddle in front of him, he would read and compose his sermons as he rode. Yet his preoccupation with religion did not keep him from a most acute observation of the manners, customs, clothes, habits, ways of life and patterns of thought of the people he met. He developed an enthusiasm for the frontier and thought it his duty to help those who came west to enjoy it as he did. He had seen that many of the migrating folk had moved in total ignorance of what they would face; that they had developed a wrong frame of mind and that they had defective equipment with which to cope with the wilderness. He determined, therefore, to write a *Guide for Emigrants to the West*. By 1837, his book had gone through several editions and become a best seller.

The tide, then, had swollen to a mighty flood. After watching it for nearly twenty years, Peck wrote in the 1837 edition of his fascinating book as vivid a description of the movement as any we may find.

Generally in all the western settlements, three classes, like the waves of the ocean, have rolled one after the other. First comes the pioneer, who depends for the subsistence of his family chiefly upon the natural growth of vegetation, called the "range," and the proceeds of hunting. His implements of agriculture are rude, chiefly of his own make, and his efforts directed mainly to a crop of corn, and a "truck patch" . . . a rude garden for growing cabbage, beans, corn for roasting ears, cucumbers and potatoes. . . . He builds his cabin, gathers around him a few other families of similar tastes and habits, and occupies his land . . . till the neighbors crowd around, roads and bridges and fields annoy him, and he lacks elbow room. . . . He "breaks for the high timber," "clears out for the New Purchase," or migrates to Arkansas or Texas to work the same process over.

The next class of emigrants purchase the lands, add field to field, clear out the roads, throw rough bridges over the streams, put up hewn log houses, . . . occasionally plant orchards, build mills, school houses, court houses, etc., and exhibit the pictures and forms of plain, frugal, civilized lives.

Another wave rolls on. The men of capital and enterprise come. The settler is ready to sell out and . . . push farther into the interior. The small village rises to a spacious town or city. . . . Broadcloths, silks, leghorns, crepes and all the refinements, luxuries, elegancies, and fashions are in vogue. Thus wave after wave is rolling westward: the real *el dorado* is further on.

A portion of the first two classes remain stationary amidst the movement, improve their habits and conditions, and rise in the scale of society.

We see here the strange lure working, forever beckoning the people on! It is no wonder that Americans believed they saw the hand of God leading them—that for the waves to move as far as the land went was the "Manifest Destiny" of the United States. Yet we notice too that only a part of the groups moved on from each point; that a part stayed where they were till they were joined by others from the rear. It is easy to see here the different temperaments of the men and women composing the migrating horde: the eternally restless and the easily content; those who must have adventure and those who most want security; those who reach out for loneliness in the freedom of uninhabited country and those who are dependent on the warmth and strength of others, who love society and are happiest in a crowd.

The restless ones moved fastest. Those who wanted to keep civilization with them moved slowly, like heavy trucks in the rear. They went no further than goods could be transported from the big eastern centers; they built carefully; made towns with streets and frame houses of sawed lumber on fieldstone foundations and they kept communications open behind their backs.

It is with the first, pioneer group that our story is now concerned. In later chapters we shall see the machinery by which industry followed the frontier and accelerated the entire movement. Watching this restless vanguard of the migration through Preacher Peck's eyes, it seems as if they needed and used no machinery at all. Here, for instance, is the way they built the shelters in which they lived:

The first buildings put up are of logs, slightly hewn on two sides and the corners notched together. The roof is made of clapboards split like staves, four feet in length, and six or eight inches in width. Two layers of these are so adjusted as to cover the cracks, and on the whole are laid heavy poles to bind down and hold the roof. This description of building is called a *"cabin."* . . . Around it are usually put up a meat or smoke house, a kitchen or cook house, a stable and corn crib, and perhaps a spring house to keep milk cool in summer. . . . The next step in advance for a dwelling is a *log house.* This is made of logs hewn on two sides to an equal thickness, the ends notched together, apertures cut through for doors and windows, a framed and shingled roof, and a brick or stone chimney. The chimney of the cabin is invariably built of sticks of wood, the largest at the bottom, and the smallest at the top, and laid up with a supply of mud or clay mortar.

In another part of his book, Peck tells us:

Hundreds of cabins are made without a nail or particle of iron about them, or a single piece of sawed plank.

Finally, confirming our suspicion that nothing resembling a machine was used by this "first wave," Peck adds:

The axe, auger, froe, drawing knife, broad axe, and cross-cut saw, are the only tools required in constructing these rude edifices; sometimes the axe and auger only are employed.

Why, then, in a history of machinery, is so much space given to these totally unmechanized frontier settlements?

To answer that question we must go back to find a piece which fits into the eastern part of our map. Again it is in Connecticut, the cradle of mass production. As we watch the pioneer chopping away the forest with blow after blow of his heavy-polled, light-bitted American ax, no mechanical sound mingles with the thuds of his blows. But multiply that ax of his by hundreds of thousands and reckon that those hundreds of thousands of axes are all going to be needed at once and it becomes evident that there has got to be machinery somewhere and that it has got to be geared to quantity production on a scale never before realized.

Several years before John Peck wrote his *Guide,* David Watkinson had a store in Hartford, Connecticut, and was helped by two nephews, Samuel and David Collins. They sold iron and steel to blacksmiths and mechanics. The steel—a metal which in those days existed only in small quantities—was used for edged tools. It was crucible steel and was imported from Sheffield, England.

Sam Collins, still in his early twenties, was a good businessman. David, eighteen, was full of ideas but, as his brother said, was "too sanguine to be cautious." Such optimists, impractical dreamers though they sometimes were, had much to do with launching the enterprises which started American industry, and it was David who gave his conservative older brother the impulse to manufacture the first instrument of the American continental conquest in truly American fashion.

David, one day, was in the shop of a blacksmith named Morgan to whom he had just delivered some Sheffield steel.

Morgan was hammering an ax on his anvil and, in an interval when he was reheating it in the forge, talked with the customer for whom the ax was being made.

"It takes so long," the customer said. "Me and my sons have got to put off going west till next summer because we can't get our axes ready.

"Here now," he went on, turning to David, "Morgan gives me the ax when he's finished with it. Edge dull, won't cut anything. I got to spend days at the grindstone, grinding it, until the stone is wore away. And the boys got to wait for their axes because there's only one stone."

On the way back to Watkinson's store David thought: Why aren't finished axes sold to these people? He spoke to his brother about this.

"A hardware store could handle them," he said, "ground and ready to use."

It took a few days for this novel thought to take root in Sam's slower mind. But in that time, a vision grew in his imagination, not of a blacksmith's shop but of a mill with trip hammers and grindstones worked by a water-wheel. It was a characteristic Yankee vision. Sam got their cousin, William Wells, interested and the three of them bought a stone grist-mill whose breast water-wheel was operated by power diverted from the Farmington River at South Canton. They had to begin with blacksmiths working by hand to establish a reputation and a market before they could think about machinery. They did, however, hitch a pump to the water-wheel which sent air through a pipe made of hollow chestnut logs to the forges. Then they made an ax design based on the experience of woodsmen, and concentrated on quality. As soon as the first sharp, finished, standardized axes were sold, the Collinses were swamped with orders. The news seemed to spread like fire among the men who had waited so long for their westward march.

In 1828, two years after the Collinses started, they installed trip hammers. They also put in grindstones six feet in diameter and a foot thick. These were quarried in Nova Scotia, sent by ship to Long Island Sound and up the Connecticut River to Hartford whence they were hauled by teams of four or six oxen to Canton. It was a laborious business but when it was done, the Collinses were able to finish some ten axes a day per workman. By 1831 they were employing about forty men.

An ax, like many of the commonest things we have, is not an easy thing to make. In the period we are exploring, they—like muskets—were made by "artists." The blacksmith was a kind of magician when he hammered out these tools because he worked with steel. Something of the old myth we find reflected in the King Arthur legends which endowed sword-makers with supernatural powers still held for the blacksmith. The reason for this was that there was no true understanding of the chemical union of iron and carbon which made steel. The artisans who worked with steel simply knew that to make an edged tool, a certain amount of heating, hammering, reheating and tempering was necessary and that, at a certain mysterious moment when the metal took on precisely the right color, the best possible tool steel was there.

The process of actually making the steel was virtually non-existent in America. The imported crucible steel was so expensive that only a little of it could be used in an ax. The head or poll, therefore, was hammered into shape from soft iron. This was then grooved and the bit, made of the fine, tough English steel was tongued into it after the application of a borax "flux" and welded by heating and hammering with a sledge and all the muscle a blacksmith had. When we see the quick welding that is done today, in airplane construction, for example; the electric welding, autogenous welding or "spot" welding that are such essential processes in every sort of metal work, it is a far cry indeed to the laborious job done in the old New England forges.

After the poll and bit had been united came the trickiest job of all. This was the tempering of the bit so that it might take the sharp, resistant edge, able to withstand daily grinding, that was necessary to the work of the backwoodsman in a virgin forest. "Tempering" is a process of heating to a certain degree and then plunging into a cold brine bath. Chemically, it is getting the right ratio of iron and carbon in the steel. Today we can figure this with precision. In the old days, when (in America at least) the chemistry was largely unknown, tempering was a matter of highly intuitive guesswork and that was a thing in which one man was likely to be immensely superior to another because of native gifts.

Work with tool steel consisted mainly of getting it to a point where it was neither too brittle nor too soft. Too much tempering made it extremely hard but almost like glass in brittleness. It was impossible, however, with the early methods of heating and plunging it hot, in the bath, not to temper it too much. It became necessary, afterward, to "draw" some of the temper out. This was done by a slow reheating. During this the metal changed color. When it had attained a certain "precise" hue—meaning when the blacksmith's practiced eye was satisfied—the temper was said to be sufficiently drawn. The color was called "pigeon blue." To make sure, the blacksmith laid his ax-poll on the anvil and struck the edge sharply with a hammer. If it splintered too easily, more temper must be "drawn out."

We can see how difficult, therefore, was the mechanized quantity production of axes. All the Collinses were able to do was to systematize the work somewhat and to install machines which replaced the blacksmith's muscle but not his eye. A trip hammer consists of a weight mounted on the end of a pivoted bar. The bar is raised to a certain point and is released by a cam mechanism so that it falls by gravity. It is then again raised. By proper gearing to a power source such as a water-wheel, a trip hammer may give a series of rapid successive blows. This hammering continues until the mechanism is interrupted by a "trip" operated by a foot pedal. With a trip hammer a blacksmith was able to turn out an ax job more quickly and, at the same time, spare his muscles. We cannot, however, call this "mechanization" in a production sense. The Collins mill was therefore at a stage not far removed (except for the big wheel grinding) from the blacksmith's forge in 1832. In that year one of the most remarkable characters in our story entered the little establishment at Collinsville. It was he who first made axes available in large quantity for the western advance and later, in another characteristically American industry which we shall discover in a later chapter, achieved one of the longest strides in the progress toward mass production.

Elisha King Root became fascinated by machinery at the age of ten and the spell of it never left him. He was a bobbin boy at ten—a common job for children since the beginning of the textile industry—and, a few years later, was apprenticed to a machinist in Ware, Massachusetts. It is probable that machinists in that region were mainly concerned with cotton mill machinery. In Chicopee Falls—one of the cradles of machine-tool making where Root followed this trade on his own—he undoubtedly worked at other kinds of simple machines. He was twenty-four when he applied to the Collinses for a job in their ax mill.

Old-timers at the Collins plant—it is flourishing today— still tell of the rumpus Root caused after a few days in the forge room. No one, of course, can remember this, but Root has become a kind of legend in Collinsville. Root thought all the machinery ought to be scrapped. The man in charge, known as Uncle Ben, was a conservative and started an argument which is said to have lasted for years. It was the old artisan tradition in conflict with the new revolutionary Yankee mind which knew that the time had come when machines must replace men as far as possible. Samuel Collins, however, was a sensible man and, himself, an adventurer in new fields so Root won out.

Unfortunately for us, Root was too deeply absorbed in mechanical engineering to blow his own horn. He insisted on getting his ideas and his inventions adopted but once that was done he cared nothing for the credit. The result was that, except for certain patent records, few details of his life remain. His name is almost forgotten because our historians have been more interested in the heroes of politics and the battlefield than in those of industry.

We do know of the extraordinary jump in production of axes made by the company in the first ten years after Root's arrival. His first and greatest interest was in machines for forging. These were various kinds of hammers beginning with the trip variety but using dies for shaping the metal. These dies were made in the exact shape desired, the hot piece of metal was placed between them and the hammer came down, repeating its blows in rapid succession. Later, when steam hammers and "drop" forging came in, the quick repetition was unnecessary. Root's forging machines shaped the ax-poll with the groove in it ready for the bit and completed the welding.

The most important machine was one which punched the "eyes" or holes for the hickory handles in the solid ax-polls. Formerly a slow process of hammering thin the metal on one side of the poll, then bending it into a loop and welding it had been practiced. Root's machine made an eye of standard size and shape into which a properly shaped handle would fit without fail. It eliminated fussy whittling and resulted in an ax the woodsman could use with certainty that the poll and handle would not part company.

A great part of Root's reform came in the arrangement of machines and furnaces so as to save the steps of the workman. He also managed an efficient division of labor. He analyzed all the operations which must be performed and made each man a specialist in a single operation. All of these things were parts of the Whitney system. There can be little doubt that, even in his early days as a machinist, he had heard of and understood this system, for Chicopee Falls was at that time already making machines for the Springfield Armory to be used in the interchangeable parts manufacture of firearms.

Another significant change took place in the difficult tempering job. Both the furnace for the original tempering and that for the drawing were made circular. Within them circular drums revolved. On these axes were hung, their bits in the furnace flames, so that every ax would get the same treatment—rapid or slow heating, depending on how fast the drums were revolved. Each of these drums held a hundred or more ax-polls. This fact signalized the new age: "one at a time" had given way to "a hundred at once."

Jigs were used extensively to secure a uniformity which no machining by eye could ever attain. In the operation of grinding at the great wheels, jigs held the ax-polls with their bits against the stones. These enabled the operator to exert a precise amount of pressure. One ingenious device of this sort was a kind of saddle in which the operator sat and to which the jig was attached so that he could communicate pressure through shifting the weight of his body. All these things eliminated the need for skill so that untrained workers could carry on much of the work. Ax-making never acquired the degree of fool-proof mechanical perfection we find in some industries: any manufacture involving forge or foundry work still requires artisans. Its importance to our story comes from the fact that its quantity production answered the first pioneer need and brought the possibility of speed to the frontier movement.

One other contribution it made was in giving national validity to a trade-mark. Because of the standard excellence of Collins tools, the device with its arm and hammer which was stamped on every one became known and remembered like the hall-mark or the word "sterling" on silver. We are so accustomed to trade-marks today, when there are so many it is not easy to choose among them, that we find it difficult to picture a time when they were rare. But the trade-mark's importance then came largely from the fact that goods so stamped came to outsell the local, small-unit brand and so brought about that condition which, today, we describe as "nation-wide." In 1954, national brands have driven out everything else. As recently as fifty years ago one went to a grocer and asked for a quart of oatmeal or corn meal. He dug it out of a bin and put it in a bag. No one knew who ground the meal. Today these things are packaged and trade-marked by the maker. Similarly one once went to a hardware store and asked for an ax. The purchaser looked it all over carefully, balanced it, swung it, and decided for or against it. The time came, however, when he asked for a Collins ax and did not bother to examine it.

This is merely an example of what was happening. The Collins trade-mark was not unique even in 1840. There were plenty of others on other manufactures. But the use of trade-marks, the common acceptance of brand names, and the development of certain kinds of factories in particular centers and the sending out of things from those centers all over the world are essential parts of the great complex of mass production. The Collinses were not, perhaps, unique in any sense but they were pioneers and everything they did was characteristically American.

So, with axes and mattocks and plows made by the Collinses and other Yankees, great stretches of forest and prairie land were cleared and made ready for planting. As we have seen, those who first started farms worked on a small scale, cultivating only enough for them to live on, but after the restless, pioneer wave had passed on, real farmers discovered the depth, richness and stonelessness of the western soil. These planted not merely for subsistence but to sell the produce back east. They found that grain—especially wheat and corn—grew in such fabulous quantity that soon they were unable to harvest it. An entire family—and pioneer farmers' families were large—would be able only to cut, stack and thresh a few acres. The sight of the vast unharvested fields, in which they had so hopefully planted, drove these men to despair.

Again we must find a piece for our puzzle somewhere in the east before we can fit in the golden pieces that represent the prairie wheat lands.

This time it is in the state of Virginia.

CHAPTER SIX

Wheat

THE FARMER looked up at the sound of hooves. Above him, astride a horse, sat a long-limbed man with a shock of black hair and a half-circle of black beard under his chin. The farmer put down his cradle-scythe with which, through the hot day, he had been cutting wheat.

"Well, stranger," he said.

The horseman did not smile.

"You can't cut it in time," he said.

"I don't need you to tell me that."

"I can show you how to do it."

The farmer stared at him without speaking.

"Not this harvest," the stranger went on. "It's too late. I suppose you'll turn the hogs in here now. I've seen that coming through Ohio."

"I've got to, haven't I? My wife, three boys, two girls are working all day. Even the women. That's how it's got to be on the prairie, stranger. You're from the east. You don't know. Of course we planted too much, you'll say. Well, with the rising price of wheat . . ."

"Yes, there's a fortune here. I never saw anything like these prairies. I didn't believe it till I saw it. Well, go ahead and plant as much next year and you'll reap all of it."

He reached down and held out his hand.

"My name is McCormick. I'm from Virginia. I've got a machine that will cut fifteen or more acres of grain in a day."

The farmer shook hands and smiled doubtfully.

"I've heard something about machines. I haven't heard much that's good."

"Will you read this?"

The farmer turned away from the sun and read the fine print on the sheet McCormick had handed him. He read all of it slowly.

"These eastern farmers . . . We don't know about this out here."

"It's harder to reap eastern grain than prairie grain," McCormick said. "The fields are hilly and have stones in them. My reaper would work far better here. If these men speak well of it, you can be sure of it."

The farmer handed back the paper.

"I haven't got a hundred dollars," he said.

"You'll make five times that from the harvest."

"Maybe. The hundred dollars has got to come first."

Cyrus McCormick thought for a while. The idea in his mind had been growing during the last weeks as he had journeyed through Pennsylvania and Ohio to Illinois where the vastness of the prairie had taken his breath away. He had seen fields of wheat wasted in spite of the day and night work of the families—sometimes with German or Irish immigrants helping. The harvest only lasted a few days before the fine ripe grain broke and rotted. McCormick knew that his Virginia reaper would more than pay for itself in a day's work.

"Will you do this?" he said. "My agent will see you in the spring. He will deliver a reaper to you. You need not pay for it until the harvest is over."

"Suppose the harvest fails? No, that ain't business, stranger."

"I know. It's a new idea. No one has done it. But maybe no one has the faith that I have in my machine."

In 1844, the summer Cyrus McCormick made his westward journey, regular installment systems were unknown. But he believed in the honesty of the prairie farmers. He had been a farmer himself so he could talk sympathetically to these people. And a western farmer looking at his stern Scotch face from which his steady eyes looked out with a kind of burning intensity was likely to believe he meant what he said.

Cyrus Hall McCormick came from rugged people. They were Scotch-Irish. His great-grandfather had come to America from Ulster in 1735. His grandfather moved from Pennsylvania to the Valley of Virginia and there between the Blue Ridge and the Alleghenies, his father had a large farm called Walnut Grove. The big brick farmhouse was the birthplace of Cyrus. He grew up surrounded by wheat. He learned the difficulty of harvesting it with a sickle or a cradle scythe in his early childhood and at fifteen he was spending many hours in the farm's blacksmith shop experimenting with devices that would make farming easier. From that time on, he was, like several of the characters we have encountered, far more attached to invention than to farming.

Most of the lads who, in the early years of the nineteenth century turned from agriculture to mechanics, had a tough time of it. We have seen the predicament of Oliver Evans. Such young men were regarded as eccentric. Farming was a noble occupation. It was hard work, sure enough, but God meant men—especially Americans—to work at the land and anyone who attempted to relieve the drudgery was suspected of laziness or, as they called it, "indolence." Cyrus McCormick was fortunate in this respect, because the ridicule and suspicion usually accorded inventors fell first upon his father.

His father, Robert McCormick, a man of considerable education, had never been able to stay long away from the forge in the log-house shop where horses were shod and implements mended. He was handy with tools; particularly apt at handling iron. Cyrus, who, even in his growing years, was so strong and hard that he seemed to be made of steel, did his chores with the grain, the cows and the horses, but the ring of the hammer on the anvil was forever in his ears and in late afternoons or on rainy days he would find his way to the shop and watch the fine red glow of the charcoal under the breath of the big bellows and the red lumps or bars of iron his father would bring under the hammer. There were saws in the shop too; chisels, hammers and other wood-working tools and Robert McCormick carved and fitted the parts of machines. So Cyrus got to working on his own, designing things which could be used on the farm. Independently, he made a cradle scythe and invented a new kind of plow for use on a hillside and he acquired in this work a mechanical imagination—a habit of reasoning things out in terms of what a machine could do.

Father and son both came to work in secrecy. Robert McCormick could not endure the contemptuous remarks and idle curiosity of the neighbors so he did his forge work behind locked doors or at night. He was a person of long patience and stubborn perseverance. He followed one dream for fifteen years. It was a horse-drawn machine for reaping grain. Again and again he built this machine and each time it failed in the field.

Finally, one evening in 1831, Robert came into the shop and said:

"I have failed, Cyrus. I shall not go on with it. I do not believe it can be done."

Cyrus was moved by his father's despair but he hid his emotion. They were not sentimental folk, these McCormicks.

"Let me try," he said.

"It's a waste of time."

"Let me try."

Cyrus went at it with a fresh mind. He had watched his father. He knew that certain things must be eliminated. Any attempt, for instance, to make a machine follow the motions made by a man must be immediately abandoned. Only a man could swing a scythe with the right curve and rhythm. A machine must cut with moving knives set on straight bars at right angles to the line on which the horses moved. These must be made to come together with a kind of scissors motion. So the rotary motion of the wheel, as the machine moved along, must be used to give a lateral motion to the cutters. Then there must be a device to straighten out the grain so that the knives could get at it, and a way of getting the grain into bundles. That was the difference between mowing and reaping. Grass could be cut and left where it fell. Wheat, oats or barley must be left in little piles with the heads all pointing the same way so it could then be bound and stacked. The sickle and the cradle scythe did this to perfection when properly handled.

Cyrus worked night and day through the summer of 1831. He was twenty-two then and tireless. By harvest time he had a new machine. It had shafts to one side so that the horse could not trample the grain. It had a large revolving reel which straightened out windblown or fallen grain ahead of the cutters. After the grain was cut, the reel, continuing its revolution, threw the cut grain back on a platform. From this, a man walking alongside, raked the grain off into piles. The raker was followed by another person who bound the piles into bundles.

Cyrus took his reaper into a field of ripe rye. It did what it was intended to do *once*. In that performance Cyrus saw that all the basic principles of the machine were right but that in detail it was crude. It was clumsy, noisy, easily broken. It frightened all but the most phlegmatic farm horses. It worked only when conditions of weather, ripeness of the grain and evenness of the ground were right.

Thirteen years passed before Cyrus McCormick was sure enough of his machine to know that his guaranty to the Illinois farmer was safe. Part of that time was spent on a venture with his father in the smelting of iron ore from a local deposit into pig iron in a home furnace. They did this to make money enough for Cyrus to build new reapers. The venture was a disaster through no fault of the McCormicks but because of a crash of prices in the iron market. It plunged the whole family into debt and the prosperous farm was mortgaged. It is said that the sheriff arrived one day to foreclose the mortgage, but that after talking to the McCormicks he was so impressed with their honesty, their industry and their stubborn fortitude in the face of catastrophe that he rode away without serving his writ.

By 1844 Cyrus had greatly improved his machine. He had shown it in western New York and in Ohio, but most of the sales he had made were to farmers in the Valley of Virginia. It was bad country for any but the most perfect machine to work in. Some of the farmers were entertained by his exhibitions; others were contemptuous or angry when there was an imperfect performance.

There is a story about one of these shows which is probably true; at any rate it is typical of the varying views of the time and place. Cyrus got permission from a farmer at Lexington, Virginia, to give a public exhibition in his wheat field. A hundred people came. The field was rough and hilly and the reaper shook violently as it cut. Presently the farmer ran up to McCormick in a rage.

"Stop your horses! You are rattling the heads off my wheat!"

It is said that the spectators were quick to join in a chorus of jeers; that even the Negro slaves laughed at the failure. At this point, however, an impressive person whose presence subdued the crowd walked up to Cyrus who had halted his work and said:

"I'll give you a fair chance, young man. That field of wheat on the other side of the fence belongs to me. Pull down the fence and cross over."

Cyrus thanked him and cut six acres of his wheat without a hitch. The spectators then changed their tune and the reaper was driven in a procession to Lexington and placed on view in the public square where anyone could examine it and praise it.

These ups and downs followed one another over the years. Meanwhile other inventors built machines. One persistent and, for a time, quite successful, rival was a Quaker from Maine, blind in one eye, who had made his invention under handicaps. One of his difficulties was that although brilliant in his understanding of mechanics, this Obed Hussey had been a sailor, not a farmer, and thus had never absorbed the reaping technique into his blood and bones, so to speak, as a farmer must. Another trouble was his poverty. Yet with all these drawbacks, he had shown his machine in six states before McCormick had moved outside of Virginia and even in Cyrus's own valley he had won recognition. His machine was sturdier and simpler than McCormick's: its disadvantage was that it was a better mower than it was a reaper. It cut grass beautifully.

But when it worked in wheat it required more horsepower and more manpower to do a complete reaping job.

The comparison between McCormick and Hussey points one of the important morals of our story. There can be no doubt of Hussey's ingenuity and perseverance although some of McCormick's admiring biographers play down these qualities as did McCormick himself through a series of bitter lawsuits. Given substantial backing and wise advice, Hussey might have gone on to the magic success which those pregnant years promised inventors of agricultural machines. But by himself he lacked McCormick's intuition. When these two inventors arrived at the crossroads of their careers, Hussey took the wrong turning and McCormick the right one. It was McCormick who allied himself with the trend of the time, the vast waves of migration and the movement toward continental conquest.

Hussey began his reaper building in Cincinnati close to the point of the frontier wedge. Everything favored him then. The western field lay clear before him. In Ohio, he was nearly ten years ahead of McCormick. Yet at this point he turned to the east. He moved to Baltimore and went on with his work there. This was partly because a friend in Baltimore had offered him backing. But, in those days of difficult transportation, it was a move which was destined, in the long run, to be fatal. You could not, then, when the trend was so strong, when the suction of the western vacuum was so insistent, go against it and survive. Not, in any case, if your stock in trade was a large, clumsy and breakable machine which had to travel on rivers and canals and wagons on muddy roads. In a way Hussey's move was comparable to Eli Whitney's withdrawal to New Haven to make his agricultural machine—away from his enormous market.

At the same crossroads in 1844, McCormick turned his face in the direction the caravans of wagons and pack animals and river boats were traveling. He had sold some machines in Virginia. He had enthusiastic testimonials from Virginia farmers. But tales of the land across the Alleghenies had filtered even into the conservative old Virginia Valley where the Pennsylvania Dutch, and religious groups such as the Mennonites, had settled into deep-rutted ways of life.

"In Virginia," he said one day to his father, "the reaper is a luxury. Over there, across the mountains, I think it is a necessity. Anyway, I'm going to find out."

He put his last money, $300, in his belt, the testimonial letters in his pocket and started out. By this time, however, he was in a position to deliver—or so he believed—if orders came in. He had already shipped seven reapers west and although they had to travel by ship down the James River, along the Atlantic and Gulf coasts to New Orleans, thence up the Mississippi and finally up the Ohio to Cincinnati, he knew the job was possible.

His western journey covered three thousand miles and took, altogether, some two years. In the course of it he made one serious mistake and had one brilliant idea. The idea was what turned him, almost overnight, into a millionaire and may have altered the history of the United States. It is impossible to say that if the idea had not come to McCormick it would not have come to someone else.

The question is: Would it have come in time? McCormick found his idea in a dreary little town built on a partially filled swamp on the edge of Lake Michigan.

McCormick's mistake—and it is important to our story because it shows the early need for concentration and a kind of "dictatorship" in mass-production industry—was in licensing various manufacturers to build his reapers instead of supervising the manufacture himself. He did this in western New York, in Ohio, in Missouri and in Illinois. The result was the direct opposite of mass production. (This can be done more easily today when machinery, patterns, specification sheets, materials and so on are standardized.) Every licensed manufacturer turned out a different reaper. Each incorporated ideas of his own and turned out what he thought was a prettier or more efficient job. From the customers came a variety of protests. The reapers were not as represented, not as advertised, not as promised. McCormick checked as quickly as he could and his discovery that the complaints were all too true led him to the great decision of his life. An initial mistake, then, made him into one of the key pioneers in the mass-production chain.

The swamp town was called Chicago. It was ugly, full of jerry-built frame houses, its streets unpaved. It had gone through a dismal struggle with poverty and disease and even when McCormick first saw it the river running through it was an open sewer pouring its pungent refuse into Lake Michigan from which the town drew its drinking water. It took all of McCormick's optimism to pronounce it "healthy" because of its "bracing" off-lake breezes.

At the same time all the promise of the wealth of the middle west seemed to be concentrated there. It was a central port for the tremendous trade with the east which had opened upon completion of the Erie canal. There was a continuous water-way now to the Atlantic and near access to the Mississippi. Already in the middle 1840's railroads were pushing westward. The prophets of fortune who could see wealth even in a swamp providing it was in the right place had put their finger on it, and adventurous men like William B. Ogden and the shrewd Scot George Smith had bought thousands of acres and now were turning overnight into millionaires. Everyone was bursting with optimism; there was no cash but infinite credit; every promise was golden and apparently no one could fail.

More important, the "tycoons" of the new Chicago understood prairies; they knew that the produce of the prairies—wheat, corn and cattle—were the things that would make Chicago rich. Also, these people had no fear of "new-fangled contraptions." Everything in Chicago was new, a guess, a speculation, a venture; and people were willing to invest in schemes which, to the "stay-put" easterner were wild and visionary in the extreme. Finally, left just behind the outposts of the frontier, the city was certain to become a commercial rather than a farming center—a mecca for mechanics and ingenious Yankees who were restless yet had no itch for the soil. All these things were earmarks of a new era which new transportation had developed—first the steamboat, then canals, then railroads.

After an experiment with another citizen, McCormick went to Chicago's Number One, showed him the begin-

ning of a factory and told him his plans. This was William
B. Ogden who had come from New York State. Ogden's
brief history of his own career gives the best idea of the
kind of American he was—a kind of which there were
many examples in 1840:

I was born close to a sawmill, was left early an orphan, was
cradled on a sugar trough, christened in a millpond, graduated
at a log schoolhouse, and at fourteen found I could do anything
I tried my hand to, and that nothing was impossible. . . .

Ogden instantly grasped McCormick's power and gauged
his prospects. We may imagine the relief of the enterprising Virginian at this quick response after years of discouragement! A partnership was formed at once and they built
the largest factory in Chicago. Its instant success was one
of the fairy tales of American history; one of the bright,
romantic events which punctuate our industrial career yet
of which our history books tell us so little. In less than two
years, McCormick was able to offer Ogden a return of the
$25,000 he had invested plus $25,000 profit. Providing, he
added, that Ogden would then quit the partnership! This
request reveals an odd aspect of Cyrus McCormick.

To him the reaper was a kind of religion. By heredity
and environment a stern Presbyterian who had scarcely ever
missed a meeting and knew large portions of the Bible by
heart, he transferred some of his worship to his business.
To him it was a "calling"; God had chosen him to invent
the reaper and it was his Christian duty to promote it to
the incalculable benefit of humanity. The fact that he became a millionaire in the process in no way dimmed the

religious aura with which he endowed it. This was true of many of the pioneers in American commerce and industry. They believed in the "Manifest Destiny" of the United States, a direct demonstration of Divine Providence. This belief compensated in their consciences for much ruthlessness and dictatorship. If you believe yourself to be an instrument of God's will you feel justified in doing many things which might otherwise cause doubts.

It was with this sense—most sincerely felt—that McCormick fought Hussey and all other competitors and, indeed, defeated them. This same feeling led him to get rid of Ogden. Ogden had a hundred other interests. He was making fortunes selling real estate, putting up buildings, establishing banks. This, to McCormick, was irreverent. Anyone who was associated with the reaper must, he believed, dedicate his whole soul to it. We may ridicule or condemn such an attitude today but, right or wrong, it was what made the continental conquest possible and maintained the national integrity of the American people.

A dozen years after McCormick's factory began, that integrity was seriously threatened. McCormick's own beloved state (about which, after he left it, he was always extremely sentimental) joined with other southern states in interpreting the Constitution as permitting them to secede from the American Union. Lincoln and the North thought otherwise. It was a piece of grim irony that, in the four terrible years of conflict over this point, the Virginian's product did as much as any other single factor to defeat the land of his birth. It has often been remarked that the Yankee, Eli Whitney, always bitterly against slavery, brought about a matching irony because his cotton gin increased slavery to a point at which it became the background of the war of 1861.

If, in the decade of the 'fifties, the McCormick reaper had attained triumph, it was nothing to its success in the war years. This was because, when Lincoln called for every third able-bodied, adult man to serve the nation, the men were able to leave the farms and know that the harvest would be reaped without them. The reaper had made prairie grain-growing possible before the war; when war came it had been improved to the point where it could replace a dozen men. It was because of the reaper that America, for the first time, was able to wage a war without letting the soldiers leave the army at harvest time. It was because of the reaper that the northern armies were fed. Unhappily for the South, the greatest wheat-growing land and the most machines were all in northern territory.

This circumstance marks an interesting point in our history. Local production was no longer adequate. There must be centralized production. The materials of food must travel great distances and be processed at certain centers from which they were distributed to the remote corners of the country. The village blacksmith, butcher, miller, were being supplanted by the factory, the stockyards, the huge grain elevators and powered flour mills. Standard products poured out from centers already celebrated for particular brands. Thus clocks and watches came from Waltham and Waterbury, New Haven and Plymouth, Connecticut; meat came from mechanical butchering and dressing plants in Cincinnati and Chicago, cloth from Lawrence and Lowell and

Providence, shoes from Salem and Lynn, machine tools
from Hartford and Chicopee Falls and Windsor, Vermont.
The huge Union army received their supplies in the Civil
War from all the sections. Their demand increased quantity
production and new production machinery. It was this industrial system of which the plantation South knew almost
nothing that enabled the northern armies, despite severe
military setbacks, to win in 1865.

As we watch the powerful combine harvesters which,
today, move so rapidly over the wide western fields, reaping and threshing as they go so that clean grain falls into a
sack seconds after the standing straw has been cut, we
realize what a primitive machine the McCormick reaper
was, even at the peak of its first triumph in the 1850's.
Because the name of McCormick has become so celebrated
in connection with agricultural machinery, many believe
that he invented the improvements which made the reaper
into a harvester. This was not, however, true. None of them
were his. By the time he reached Chicago, Cyrus McCormick had ceased to be an inventor. From then on he was
a manufacturer of his own and other men's inventions.
Through years of cutthroat competition he managed to
absorb most of these. The beautiful device which bound
a sheaf of grain with twine and cast it aside—a completely
automatic performance—was invented not by McCormick
but by Charles Withington: yet the machine became a Mc-
Cormick product. Other manufacturers, however, continued
to offer dangerous rivalry until, at last, at the turn of the

century the survivors formed the International Harvester Corporation which has dominated the field ever since.

None of this fast-moving industrial triumph would have been possible but for the system devised in New Haven by Eli Whitney in the period from 1798 to 1810. A production line with a machine sequence ranged along it; the machine tools all working through jigs and fixtures were the very life and essence of Cyrus McCormick's first factory in Chicago. This is brought vividly to our attention by a newspaper account in a Chicago paper written by an astonished reporter who had just visited the factory in 1851:

You enter—little wheels of steel attached to horizontal, upright and oblique shafts are on every hand. They seem motionless. Rude pieces of wood without form or comeliness are hourly approaching them upon little railways, as if drawn thither by some mysterious attraction. They touch them and *presto,* grooved, scalloped, rounded, on they go . . . and transferred to another railway, when down comes a guillotine-like contrivance —they are mortised, bored, and whirled away. . . .

It may seem a far cry from the "little railways" to the sub-assembly conveyors in Detroit, yet as we look back from McCormick to the Evans flour mills and forward again to the River Rouge the progress seems continuous, almost uninterrupted and wholly American.

CHAPTER SEVEN

Six-Shooter

O N A HOT June day in 1844, Captain Jack Hays was glad of the cool shadows of the Nueces Canyon, and his fourteen Texas Rangers were relieved when he halted their march, told them to take the bridles off their horses and let the animals graze. One of the Rangers whose name was Noah Cherry saw a bee-tree and climbed it to get at the honey.

Texas at that time was an independent republic. It had separated itself from Mexico eight years before and was looking toward the United States with hopeful eyes. Most of its settlers had migrated there from eastern states and they wanted the government of their native country to annex this little republic and make a state of it. As it was, the settlers felt insecure. Over the Texas plains roamed one of the fiercest of American Indian tribes, the Comanche horsemen. The only protection was this body of "Rangers" which was half way between an army and a police force. In spite of it, there had been brutal massacres and kidnappings in Texas.

The little group under Hays had been out scouting for signs of Indians at the headwaters of the Nueces River. The object of the expedition was not to attack but to report the presence of Indians without being seen themselves so a larger force could be sent out from the fort at San Antonio to give battle. Small scouting parties like this had not usually been successful against large bodies of the savages as their muzzle-loading rifles could only be fired once and, while they were reloading, the Indians could ride in and do terrible damage with their arrows fired in rapid succession. There must, therefore, be enough Rangers so that they could cover one another on the reload.

The men with Hays that day had, however, another weapon beside the rifle. It was new; against Comanches it was untried. Perhaps only two of the group, Hays himself and his friend Sam Walker, had real confidence in its power.

The horses were contentedly nuzzling the lush grass and the men had loosened their belts and were stretching or lying at the edge of the cool river to drink. Suddenly Noah Cherry in the bee-tree yelled and some of the men laughed, thinking he had been stung by the bees. But as they looked at him and saw his intense expression, they stopped laughing and jumped to their feet.

"Jerusalem, captain!" Cherry shouted. "Yonder comes a thousand Indians!"

Jack Hays, though tired from the long ride, was quickly alert.

"Come down from there, quick!" he called to Cherry.

"Men, put on your bridles, take up your ropes. Be ready for them!"

Soon the Rangers saw the cloud of dust moving toward them and under it the naked yelling horsemen. None of the Rangers had ever before seen so large a body of Comanches all at once. There were not a thousand but guesses which have been made since put the number all the way from seventy to two hundred so that at the very least the Rangers were outnumbered five to one.

"We haven't a chance," one of the men said.

"Unless we can run faster than they can," someone answered. "What's Jack waiting for?"

But the captain did not order them to mount and turn. Instead he gave the command to hold their rifles at the ready.

"Now, boys," he said, "don't shoot too quick. Let them come closer. Hit something when you shoot and stand your ground. We can whip them; there can be no doubt about that."

It was the old order. Shoot your rifle dismounted—it was the only way you could be sure of your aim. But had Jack Hays lost his mind? Fourteen against these hundreds? Yet the older Rangers knew that when Hays gave an order he meant it and all of them were too well-disciplined to hesitate. When the Indians came close enough the Rangers fired. Their aim was good and several Indians and horses fell. But behind these, the others kept charging on, maddened by the loss of their comrades. The Rangers could hear the deadly arrows whiz by their ears. It must have passed through the minds of many of these brave men that the end had come; that their scalps would soon hang from the Comanches' belts. But Hays jumped into his saddle.

"After them, men! Give them no chance to turn on us. Crowd them! Powder-burn them!"

It was then that the Comanches saw something they had never seen before. In a matter of seconds it had wholly demoralized them. From his belt Captain Hays drew his new weapon and his men, now mounted, followed suit. They fired *and did not reload*. Again and again the strange little device that looked like a pistol fired its deadly bullets.

One of the Rangers told the story afterward to a friend who wrote it down so that the eye-witness account is preserved for us:

Never was a band of Indians more surprised than at this charge. They expected the rangers to remain on the defensive and to finally wear them out and exhaust their ammunition. In vain the Comanches tried to turn their horses and make a stand, but such was the wild confusion of running horses, popping pistols, and yelling rangers, that they abandoned the idea of a rally and sought safety in flight. Some dropped their bows and shields in trying to dodge the flashing pistols. The pursuit lasted three miles, and many Indians were killed and wounded.

Years later a Comanche chief who had been in the battle told how, for the first time, white men had shot their guns from the saddle.

"Each man," he said, "had a shot for every finger on his hand."

He added that his warriors had dropped off dead of their wounds along a hundred-mile trail.

So, after June, 1844, Texans knew that they had the most formidable cavalry weapon that had ever been designed. The bullets and the powder charge were loaded into the chambers of a turning cylinder at the breach. Pulling back the hammer (cocking) brought a chamber behind the hammer and locked it there. The trigger caused the hammer to strike a firing pin which in turn set off a percussion cap and fired the powder. It was only necessary then to cock the gun again and the shot could be repeated. Only one hand was necessary for the full operation.

In the late fall of 1846, Eli Whitney's son looked up from his desk in his office at the Whitneyville gun factory his father had founded and saw a stranger standing before him: a stocky man with a heavy dark brown beard and a mass of fine curled hair.

"Can you make this?" the stranger said. He threw the wooden model of a pistol on the desk. "I want a thousand in a great hurry. They're for the government. For the war. It's taken the government long enough to understand the value of my revolving pistol. Finally Captain Walker seems to have convinced them. The few the army's already got have spread terror among the Mexicans."

Whitney picked up the model and turned it over in his hands.

"Haven't you got one of the pistols?"

"No, that's the queer thing. Five thousand have been made. I can't find one. I advertised in New York. I went to every store. They must all be out west."

Whitney was examining the model carefully and admiration lighted his face.

"A revolving pistol," he said. "I've heard of them. Who was it, now, that patented it?"

"I did. Samuel Colt. I made this model from memory. It's got improvements over the others—some of them mine, some Sam Walker's. He was a Texas Ranger with Captain Hays. Now he's in our army. You'll notice this gun's a six-shooter. The old ones had only five shots."

"I'm happy to meet you, Mr. Colt," Whitney said. "I think my father's system will make these. Let me talk it over with some of my people."

This meeeting of Samuel Colt with the son of Eli Whitney was the climax of a strange, adventurous and disheartening career. Colt had been born thirty-two years before in the city of Hartford in Whitney's home state. His father was a textile manufacturer who operated, along with other business, a bleaching and dyeing establishment. This was the only part of Christopher Colt's industry which interested the boy, Sam. From his early childhood he had been fascinated by explosives. As soon as he could read, he devoured a book called *Compendium of Knowledge* which explained, among other things, gunpowder and the galvanic battery. When he was older his father gave him occasional jobs in his dyeing works from which he "borrowed" chemicals to experiment with, secretly, on leisure evenings. The secrecy was, to be sure, occasionally interrupted by explosions which shocked the countryside.

It is curious, in the light of what we know today of synthetic chemistry, to learn of the association of dyes and explosives in the mind of this boy. In the 1820's, of course, the first investigations into the subject were still nearly forty years in the future.

When Sam was fifteen, an incident occurred which marked him as a spectacularly bad boy in the community in which he lived—at that time Ware, Massachusetts. In June, 1829, the neighbors were startled by a widely circulated announcement which read:

"Sam'l Colt will blow a raft sky-high on Ware Pond, July 4 . . ."

At the pond, properly dressed for the glorious Fourth, a large crowd assembled. There was the raft, not far offshore, and, at the water's edge, Sam. He retired a moment into the bushes where he appeared to be tinkering with some sort of mechanical contrivance. Suddenly there was a violent explosion. The raft was, unfortunately, not touched —having drifted, Sam later explained, from the spot at which he had anchored it—but the mud at the bottom of Ware Pond was, indeed, blown "sky high" and descended on the holiday attire of the spectators. So! said they, it was all a practical joke! A number of young men seized Sam and were about to duck him when a stranger stepped forward and pulled back the angriest of the youth.

"Leave that boy alone," he said and, looking at him, Colt's attackers thought it wise to obey. The unknown visitor was a powerful young man whose muscles had been developed over an anvil. "This," he added, "is an important scientific experiment."

He drew Sam Colt aside and walked with him away from the crowd.

"Tell me how you did it," he said. "I'm interested because I'm a mechanic myself. I suppose you used an electric battery. But I can't understand how you got a spark to ignite a powder charge under water."

The boy was silent for a time and evidently embarrassed.

"I ought to be grateful to you, stranger," he finally said. "You saved me from a ducking. But I mean to be an inventor. An inventor has to keep things to himself."

"I guess I understand," the mechanic said. "I ought to. I expect to take out some patents myself."

He went on talking about machines. He explained mechanical drawing and the making of models. Sam was deeply interested and filed the information away in his memory. As the man left him Sam asked his name.

"I work as a millwright's machinist in Chicopee Falls," the stranger said. "I came over when I heard about your show. My name is Elisha Root."

It was a bad time for Sam Colt. His mother who had adored and indulged him was dead. His father had remarried and his stepmother was anything but sympathetic. In the fall of that year in which his submarine explosion startled Ware, his father sent him to Amherst. The following summer when the fireworks Sam had made for the Fourth set fire to a building, Amherst expelled him. He came home, told his father he wanted to be on his own. He was sick of education. He wanted to work. So his father gave him a hundred-dollar wardrobe, five dollars in cash and apprenticed him to a sea captain. This was not Sam's idea of the way he wanted to be on his own but he accepted it without complaint. The voyage from Boston to Calcutta and back took the greater part of a year. On it the sixteen-year-old boy made an invention which became the Colt revolver.

No records show how long the idea of a repeating firearm had been in his mind. He whittled his model out of a ship's block. It was a crude affair which later was called the "pepper-box" type when others tried it. It was, as Colt's definitive biographers Haven and Belden explain, "A multi-barreled arm with the barrels revolving in a block, or with the barrels in a stationary block and a revolving hammer. Either one of these systems is clumsy and inaccurate, and the idea was abandoned by Colt before his arms reached even the metal-model stage."

They reached this stage in the winter of 1831-32 in the hands of a Hartford gunsmith. By the spring of 1832, the revolver had acquired a rotating cylindrical chambered breech automatically revolved, locked and unlocked, by cocking the hammer. His father who, in enthusiasm over his son's invention, forgot past sins, had paid for the making of models up to this point. He was deeply interested. But then the money gave out and Christopher Colt who had suffered business setbacks could advance no more.

In March, 1832, Samuel left on what we would call a "lecture tour." As we read about it now it seems quaint enough. The lectures were said to be on "science." To demonstrate his knowledge of chemistry "Dr. Coult," as he called himself (supposing for some reason that the "u" added dignity), intoxicated members of his audiences with the newly discovered nitrous oxide or "laughing gas." He became an excellent showman and created a sensation wherever he went for two years. He made money enough—which was his object—to go on with the pistols.

He was able in 1836, having obtained both English and American patents, to interest some backers and a company was formed in Paterson, New Jersey, to manufacture the revolvers.

No officer or worker of this company had any understanding of the system of interchangeable parts or of the proper machinery for making precise firearms in quantity. Also, the men who had invested their money in the business seem to have been bad businessmen. Unfortunately they persuaded Colt to assign to them his patents, claiming for himself royalties and a salary. He then traveled about trying to interest people in giving him large orders. He worked especially diligently with the government but the army being then (as it always was) extremely conservative and suspicious of anything new, refused to be persuaded. Perhaps it was as well he got no large government orders as the Paterson factory could probably not have filled them. The company went into bankruptcy five years after it had started and in 1842, the factory was closed.

Nevertheless, as Colt told Whitney, some five thousand revolvers of various types were produced in the five years. Some of these found their way to Florida and were used against the Seminole Indians. Others, as we have seen, had made Texans believe that revolvers were a necessity—a matter of life and death.

In 1845, Texas was, at its own request, annexed to the

United States. Instantly there was a dispute as to its Mexican boundary. The President sent General Zachary Taylor with American troops to the spot under discussion and, within the year, the United States was at war with Mexico. Historians have come to believe that we behaved in a high-handed manner in the pursuit of this war; that the argument could have been settled by diplomacy instead of arms, and that the acquisition of the makings of five states as a result of the victory was virtually robbery. Whatever may be the rights and wrongs of this, the Mexican War was of immense value to Sam Colt. Walker, Hays and other Rangers had joined the United States Army and Walker persuaded the government to give Colt an order for a thousand revolvers and a promise to pay him $28,000 for the lot. It was then that the inventor could not find anywhere an example of his own invention to use as a model! Every gun shop in the East was sold out. Not a five-shooter or a six-shooter could be had for love or money. In his poverty after the Paterson company failed he had even sold his own personal revolvers. So he had to whittle a model. Then he borrowed money and bought back his patent rights.

Immediately after Colt left the office at Whitneyville, Whitney called in his experts to estimate on filling the order for a thousand revolvers. Obviously, as these were an entirely different proposition from muskets or rifles, entirely new machines, jigs and fixtures had to be constructed to manufacture them. The Whitney system, we remember, employed no skilled gunsmiths. The work there was not bench work. To produce these firearms rapidly and in quantity the factory had to be, as we should say, "retooled." It had to put new skills into new machines.

When Whitney told Colt this, Samuel had one of the most brilliant impulses of his life.

"When you're through with this order," he said, "I'll want those machines."

"But they'll be installed in our factory."

"I will take them away. I want them. *That must be in our contract or there will be no deal.*"

In effect these were Colt's words. It was obvious that he did not intend to let the Whitney company go on making his revolvers after this order was filled. Yet he knew that only the Whitney company would be able to put the manufacture of his revolvers on what we call a mass-production basis. The contract specifically called for "interchangeable parts." After Colt saw how this was done and had the machinery, he would be able to carry on without Whitney's assistance.

We may think that Eli's son was unwise to sign the contract. Yet it was incalculably valuable to the whole future of mass production that he did so. For in this way, the great "American System" was enabled to pass into new, fresh hands where, as we shall see, it made a spectacular advance.

Afterward Colt said he had lost money on the Whitney contract. He said the pistols Whitney produced were not as good as he could have wished. This may be partly true as, for Eli the Second, it was a new experiment and it may be doubted that the son had his father's genius. Also many new processes such as rifling the barrels, chambering the cylinders and making a number of springs, locking devices and other things had to be designed from scratch. Nevertheless, Colt by no means scorned the Whitney machinery and when in 1847, the order was completed, took it to Hartford and established a factory of his own there.

In his later years Colt was inflated by his success and inclined to give more credit to himself than to others. Today, most students of the history of mass production will give him full recognition for his invention of the revolver but little if any for the invention of the machinery for its production. In 1849, two years after the Hartford factory was established, by another intuitive stroke of genius he selected a superintendent who would so improve the Whitney system that it would be scarcely recognizable, even by the master himself, had he been alive to see it.

Whether Colt still remembered the strong-limbed mechanic who had saved him from a ducking in Ware Pond is not in the record. He did hear from the National Armory at Springfield that they had offered a large salary to the superintendent of The Collins Company at Collinsville, Connecticut, one Elisha King Root. The name may never have rung a bell in Sam's mind. But he did know that the Springfield Armory was making guns on the Whitney system and that if the armory wanted a man to carry it on badly enough to pay him so well, he, Colt, wanted him more.

It is said that the offer he made to Root was larger than any ever made in American industrial history up to that time. The Collinses must have been sorry to lose the genius who had made it possible for them to sell so many hundreds of thousands of axes to frontiersmen. Yet there is a limit to the potential design of ax-making machinery. To Root, in

1849, as he examined Colt's beautiful, precise instrument, the possibilities of machinery to make *that* must have seemed infinite. In any case he took the job and within a few years the Colt Armory at Hartford and the branch Colt works in England had become two of the wonders of the world.

It is important to consider the London factory. It was not customary in those pre-Civil War days for American industrialists to work internationally in this way. It is true that many American goods were exported. But to set up a complete manufacturing establishment abroad and there make a piece of mechanism precisely as it was made at home was an extraordinary venture. We may mark it as a step toward present-day mass distribution as well as a kind of archetype for the kind of mass production with which the Ford and the Singer people and many others now cover the world. The fact, however, that Colt, after a short period, had to abandon the London enterprise because British workers could not adjust to it shows how far apart the two nations were, industrially, in the 1850's.

Happily we have a detailed description of this fabulous London plant which was published in 1855 in a magazine called *Household Words,* edited by Charles Dickens.

Under the roof of this low, brickbuilt, barrack-looking building . . . we may see what cannot be seen elsewhere in all England, the complete manufacture of a pistol, from dirty pieces of timber and rough bars of cast steel, till it is fit for the gunsmith's case. To see the same thing in Birmingham and in other places where firearms are made almost entirely by hand labour, we should have to walk about a whole day, visiting many shops car-

rying on distinct branches of the manufacture. . . . Neat, deli-
cate-handed little girls do the work that brawny smiths still do
in other gun shops. Most of them have been sempstresses and
dressmakers, unused to factory work. . . . Even the men have,
with scarcely an exception, been hitherto ignorant of gun-making. No recruiting sergeant ever brought a more miscellaneous
group into the barrack-yard, to be drilled more rapidly to the
same duty, than these two hundred hands have been. Carpenters,
cabinet-makers, ex-policemen, butchers, cabmen, hatters, gas-
fitters, porters . . . are steadily drilling and boring at lathes all
day in the upper rooms.

Could anything be more revealing of the march toward
mass production which had been made in the thirty years
since the death of Eli Whitney? Already, this Pimlico factory seems to smell of modern Detroit. And this piece by a
startled reporter in the London periodical shows as nothing
else could, the rapt astonishment—almost incredulity—of
Englishmen at this strange magic of the "skilled machine."
Yet Colt had to give it up. There was too much prejudice
and ignorance, taxes and red-tape.

The Hartford Armory, however, continued to grow. The
description of this in the *United States Magazine* in 1857 is
calmer but no less revealing of "production in series" as we
call a part of mass production today.

Each portion of the firearm has its particular section. As we
enter . . . the first group of machines appears to be exclusively
employed in chambering cylinders; here another is boring barrels; another group is milling the lock frames; still another is
drilling them; beyond are a score of machines boring and screw-

ing the nipples . . . here are the rifling machines . . . now we come to the jigging machines that mortice out the lock frames. . . .

Most of it was designed and arranged by Elisha King Root. A few patents are in Colt's name but it is nearly certain that Root played a part in every invention except those in the actual revolver itself. Even here Root made contributions. We have the specifications and drawings of many of his beautiful machines including borers and riflers. When at last Colt died in 1862—the second year of the Civil War in which his revolvers played so important a part—Root found his proper reward and became president of the Colt Company.

Looking, today, at some of the crime waves that have swept our more compact, later society, we are inclined to wonder whether Sam Colt's invention has not, in the long run, done more harm than good. We cannot, however, doubt that it immensely quickened our settlement of the Great Plains or that the methods of its making advanced the progress toward mass production in a way that perhaps no other device could have done.

CHAPTER EIGHT

Time Machines

As the years drew toward the mid-nineteenth century, a number of writers from overseas —especially Englishmen—came to the United States, traveled in the frontier West, were fascinated by what they saw and wrote about it when they got home. One Briton, a distinguished scientist with the impressive name of Featherstonehaugh, was astonished at finding, in almost every cabin, no matter how lowly, one luxurious possession which had come there from far away New England.

Wherever we have been [he wrote in 1844], in Kentucky, in Indiana, in Illinois, in Missouri, and . . . in every dell of Arkansas, and in cabins where there was not a chair to sit on, there was sure to be a Connecticut clock.

It had, the Englishman explains, invariably been brought by an itinerant peddler whose words he reports with the Americanisms in italics.

The clock peddler is an irresistible person; he enters a log cabin, gets familiarly acquainted with its inmates in the shortest imaginable time and then comes on business.

"I *guess* I shall have to sell you a clock before I go."

"I *expect* a clock's of no use here; besides, I ha'nt got no money to pay for one."

"Oh, a clock's fine company here in the woods; why you couldn't live without one after you'd had one awhile, and you can pay for it some other time."

"I *calculate* you'll find I ain't agoing to take one."

The wife must now be acted upon.

"Well, mistress, your husband won't take a clock. . . . I suppose, however, you've no objection to my nailing one up here, till I come back in a month or so. I am sure you'll take care of it, and I shall charge you nothing for the use of it at any rate. . . ."

This is not, perhaps, the precise way television sets are sold one hundred years later, but it is close enough to make us wonder at the remote origins of some of our commonest customs—some of which still amaze Englishmen and other Europeans. The television salesman, of course, is honest, and his set is reliable. With the clock peddler of a century ago this was not always the case. Mr. Featherstonehaugh goes on to explain what happened after the clock was on the wall. When the peddler left, his words came true. The clock became such a source of delight to the couple and especially to the children, that, by the time the peddler returned they could not, indeed, live without it. So they gave him a note for the money (eighteen or twenty dollars) and in six months he came to collect it. The clock, they would tell him, had stopped. Nothing would make it go. The peddler had expected this. He had brought a new clock with him. Cheerfully he hung it in place of the old one and, followed by the blessings of the people, he went to his next customer and exchanged their clock too, hanging the one he had just unhung in its place. He had given it a hasty going-over—enough to make it tick for a day or so. Continuing in the same way "he changes the clock at every place he stops . . . favoring every one of his customers with the bad clock of his neighbor."

The upshot of the system was that, although, as our English informant tells, there was a clock in every cabin, only a few of them gave anything resembling the correct time if, indeed, their movement had not entirely ceased.

To find out why this was so, we must return with the peddler to his headquarters. The "Yankee peddler" was an institution which had begun in long-past colonial days. His function had always been to penetrate the wilderness where the settlers had no stores or other means of purchasing their needs. He sold brooms, tinware, coffee grinders, buttons, pins, cloth and a quantity of ingenious gadgets of all sorts: indeed, the American addiction to gadgetry today may be traced to the Yankee peddler. He also peddled news, gossip, tall stories which he made up, and brought friendliness and cheer into the loneliest places. His visits, months apart, were looked forward to with the greatest eagerness and if the frontier folk were sometimes swindled, the accepted reason was because they weren't "smart." Also there were honest men as well as sharp traders among these traveling merchants and some were hard-pressed by the difficulties of transportation and of collecting payment.

The mechanical device for measuring time is probably the oldest automatic machine there is. It does for man something he cannot possibly do for himself. The best man can do unaided is to tell day from night and, if there is sunlight, morning from afternoon. Perhaps if he is experienced in observing the stars he can make guesses at the hours if the night sky is bright. But for any schedule of work or appointments, he must have a clock.

A clock or watch is such an individual necessity today that it is difficult to imagine a time when these things were luxuries. Yet as recently as the early nineteenth century even a bad watch was like a precious jewel: in colonial and revolutionary times the possession of a clock signified wealth. In England this was more or less true as late as the 1840's.

Most people relied on a public clock in a church steeple or the cupola of a town hall whose striking could be heard at a distance. The tempo of life, however, was slower: if a man was not on the dot for his appointment, it did not greatly matter; no doubt the person awaiting him was also uncertain about the time. Travel was, as we have seen, extremely slow: if a stage coach or a river boat was a day late in its arrival after a short trip, no one was greatly concerned. Yet, as the nineteenth century advanced the American speed impulse grew rapidly. Steamboats were racing up and down the rivers in the 1840's and soon after that, railroads were competing to shorten time-tables. This is one reason why time-measuring machines became universal in the United States while they were still luxuries abroad.

Another reason was the need of people on lonely farms or remote frontiers for some way of keeping track of the passing hours. There is a direct connection between the movement of the frontiers and the increase in American clock production. The other reasons were the same as those which turned the automobile from a luxury to a universal possession: the equality concept making every American believe he was "as good as the next man" and the American system of interchangeable parts manufacture.

But our question after reading Mr. Featherstonehaugh's report remains unanswered. Why, all over the frontiers, did the Englishman find that the beautiful Connecticut clocks had stopped?

It was because their works, their wheels, were made of wood.

In a reasonably dry, cool climate, a wooden-wheeled clock will go along indefinitely keeping pretty good time. In museums, antique shops and the houses of collectors today, some of the old clocks do very well because they are kept in a constant temperature with unchanging relative humidity. But in 1800, at the seashore, in hot, humid southern swampland or aboard ship, the cherry and laurel parts of an American clock would swell and warp until distortion stopped the works. Nevertheless, wooden clocks were the cheapest and most widely used American-made time-pieces from 1790 to the 1830's and it was to them that Eli Whitney's American system was first applied.

There were, of course, better clocks—for the rich. There were fine "grandfather" clocks with brass works which ran for a week without rewinding, imported from England, and clocks in marble and ormolu cases from France or Germany. American-made brass clocks were all eight-day affairs. The reason for this was that brass clocks were all expensive and persons extravagant enough to buy one were not supposed to be content with something which had to be wound every day. Almost all the clocks of the period were propelled by weights as the art of tempering steel for springs had not been learned—at least by Americans.

The quantity production of clocks began in Connecticut in the first decade of the nineteenth century. One reason why clocks were a Connecticut specialty was that most of the early "Yankee peddlers" were Connecticut men with a brand of ingenuity which adapted itself to the manufacture as well as the sale of clocks. In the handicraft period many men were both makers and sellers of clocks; if they had no peddler's wagon or traveled where there were no roads, they rode horseback with the clocks strapped to the saddles. In the handicraft days the clockmaker usually made only the works, the customer having the case made to his order by a cabinet-maker.

In a tiny village which was called successively Northbury, Plymouth Hollow and Terryville, a young man named Eli Terry bought a mill about 1802 and used water power to turn certain machinery for the making of clocks. Historians are in conflict about how Terry learned his trade but undoubtedly he had been apprenticed as a boy to a maker or repairer of clocks. In any case, he seems to have been the first to use water power for this delicate operation and the neighbors, hearing about it, and hear-

ing some of the claims he was making, tapped their heads
and suggested that all of Terry's wheels were not in his
clocks. We do not know what the first machinery was—
probably a lathe—but there is every indication that he
soon made a division of labor of the Whitney kind because he mystified his friends saying he was *starting* two
dozen, and, later, several hundred clocks *at once*. On the
handicraft system he could not have *started* ten or twenty
or a hundred clocks unless he had had ten or twenty or
a hundred workmen.

Between 1802 and 1807, he undoubtedly learned something about what Whitney was doing in a New Haven
suburb, because in the latter year he took an order for
four thousand clocks. The citizens of Plymouth then gave
him up as incurable. His schedule of producing these is
entirely in keeping with Whitney's musket timetable.
The first year was spent in making the machinery ("tooling") to make four thousand clocks. In the second year one
thousand and in the third year three thousand actual clocks
were made. When the order was finished Terry was rich
and all the Plymouth doubters became his friends and ad-
mirers.

It is a pity that we have so few clues to Terry's machinery.
One of the machines was certainly a lathe for cutting the
teeth in a number of cogged wheels at once with such precision that all the wheels were enough alike to be picked at
random for the assembly. Others must have been jigged
machine tools of a relatively primitive sort for the making
of identical plates, dials, pallets and other parts.

Having filled his first order, Terry sold out to his partners

Seth Thomas and Silas Hoadley who immediately started on their own and they in turn spawned other clock factories so that soon there were many establishments in nearby towns all using the plan of equipment and the kind of machinery that Terry had installed. By 1820, Terry himself had standardized a certain type of "shelf clock," (in much the same way that Henry Ford standardized his Model T) and from then on, he was regularly turning out ten thousand clocks a year. In 1835, nearly a hundred thousand clocks were being produced annually in the towns of Bristol, Plymouth and Farmington and these were carried by peddlers to every part of the country and on all the frontiers the state of Connecticut was blessed or cursed according as its clocks ran or stopped.

Terry was the pioneer but he was not the real hero of our clock story as it bears on the general mass-production scheme. This was one of his workers, an extremely enterprising artisan and a true production genius named Chauncey Jerome. Fortunately for us, Jerome, in a rather melancholy old age after he had been pursued by hard luck, wrote his autobiography so we know more about him than we do about Terry.

"The ticking of a clock," Jerome said, "is music to me," and it was his ambition to have Jerome clocks ticking in every corner of the world: in African jungles and in the paper houses of Japan as well as in the capitals of Europe. The longer he worked, however, at the business of making and peddling clocks, the more certain he became that there were places in which the music he loved would not be heard as long as its instruments were made of Connecticut cherry and laurel.

Chauncey Jerome was born in Canaan, Litchfield County. His father was a blacksmith and miserably poor. The boy was taken from school at nine and set to making nails in his father's shop. At eleven, his father died and from then on he had to find his own means of support, working for farmers. At sixteen he wandered to the already thriving clock center of Plymouth and got a job with a carpenter there. As all the artisans of Plymouth were working on some part of a clock, Chauncey's allotted task was dial-making for the grandfather variety. He left this to fight in the War of 1812 and when that was over, he got work with Terry who was moving rapidly toward the peak of his prosperity. It was in the Terry shop that Jerome's life's ambition came upon him.

He was in business on his own when he worked out his first profitable idea. This was to put a mirror in the front of a clock below the dial. This hardly seems to us a stroke of genius. But then we are surrounded by mirrors; and other bright objects of chromium and stainless steel are common-places. In the drabness of country life in the 1820's "looking glasses," as mirrors were called, were rare. To have one combined with a clock so that every time you looked to see the hour you also saw yourself was as exciting then as some of our fantastic new electrical gadgets are to us. So the "looking-glass clock" started a fad which, in a few years, spread south and west, and Jerome's enlarged factory leaped into the lead in Connecticut clock production.

Jerome then did an interesting thing which shows to what

extent the Whitney system had adapted itself to clock manufacture. By the mid-1830's, Southerners had grown so an-
noyed by the flood of clock peddlers from the North that
laws had been passed putting a prohibitive price on licenses
to outsiders. It was all right, for instance, for citizens of Virginia to peddle clocks in Virginia but no more Yankees!
Whether the Connecticut peddlers had sold too many al-
leged "wooden nutmegs" or whether the word "dam-
yankee" had already been coined for some other reason
made no difference to Jerome. He was threatened with the
cutting off of a considerable market for his clocks or, at
least, a reduction of profits through working with too many
middlemen. He therefore took the unheard-of step of establishing an *assembly plant* in Richmond. To it, he shipped
the parts from his factory in Connecticut and in it he produced finished clocks. Virginians, who had never heard of
interchangeable parts, naturally supposed the entire manufacturing operation had taken place in Richmond.

The people [Jerome tells us in his autobiography] were highly
pleased with the idea of having clocks all made in their own
state. The old planters would [say] they meant to go to Richmond and see the wonderful machinery there must be to produce
such articles.

This was in 1835. The following year he started a similar
establishment in South Carolina. All this time, however,
Jerome, though prospering in his business, was growing increasingly discontented with the limitations of the wooden
clock works. Then, in the terrible panic year of 1837, when
dozens of clockmakers were forced out of business, Jerome

hit upon the idea which was to bring his greatest success and make the American cheap clock celebrated not only in America but throughout the world.

In the Connecticut town of Waterbury, a whole new industry had grown up since the turn of the century. It was founded upon a novel method of working brass—an alloy of copper with zinc—which was far cheaper than the old process of casting it in molds. This was rolling it into sheets. From these sheets any desired shape could be punched out by dies under the drop hammer.

Why this industry should have started in Waterbury is another question that can probably be answered by the peddler. Since the beginning of their business, brassware was one of the peddlers' stocks in trade. Whether domestic or imported, brass pots and kettles, warming pans, lamps and buttons hung and jangled in their carts. These became known everywhere as "Yankee notions."

In a southern cabin one night after a visit to one of his branch plants, Jerome got to wondering about brass clocks. If you could make an eight-day brass clock, why should you not make a one-day brass clock? Might not a one-day clock made with stamped instead of cast wheels be produced at low cost? Was not this idea that a brass clock must have an eight-day movement, must be carefully built by hand, must, in short, be a luxury—was not this whole notion simply a prejudice based on old, outworn handicraft methods?

In this thinking Chauncey Jerome was repeating the thought that has occurred to American inventors since the beginning of American society and continues to this day to dominate the American inventive mind. In every period we find men asking—as Henry Ford asked—why must this or that thing be a luxury; why can it not become the possession of every man, of every American citizen, *each one of whom is as good as his neighbor?* And the answer—at least since Whitney—has always been: Quantity, speed, economy of labor, proper division of work into departments, the correct grouping of machines and continuity of production.

Chauncey Jerome at the birth of his idea rushed home. There, with the businesses of his neighbors falling all about him, he got stamped wheels from Waterbury, cut their teeth a stack at a time with perfected gear-cutting lathes. The result was an accurate one-day brass clock which sold, in the depression years, for six dollars in competition with ten and fifteen dollar wooden clocks. In four years after he began this manufacture he was producing clocks which sold at retail for $1.50 and, at that price, brought a handsome profit to their maker. Eventually, when he was able to concentrate the whole manufacture including the stamping of the wheel blanks in his own factory, he was able to write:

It will no doubt astonish a great many to know how rapidly [the clocks] can be made. I will venture to say that I can pick out three men who will take the brass in the sheet, press out and level under the drop, then cut the teeth and make all the wheels to five thousand clocks, in one day. There are from eight to ten of these wheels in every clock. . . . This will look to some like a great story, but is one of the wonders of the clock business. If some of the parts of the clock were not made for almost nothing, they could not be sold so cheap when finished.

After 1840, Jerome was no longer content with a domestic market for his product. Now that the wheels could be counted on not to warp in the salt sea air, he decided to ship them abroad. He sent, therefore, a large consignment to England in the care of his son, Chauncey, junior. The value marked on these was $1.50 each which was considerably higher than their cost. When the British customs inspectors looked at the consignment they went into a rage against young Chauncey.

"So," they said, "you're trying to cheat us out of the duty that ought to be paid on these clocks."

Jerome's son did not understand and said so.

"A dollar and a half!" said one of the inspectors. "For a clock like that! Why, a pound sterling wouldn't cover the cost of making such a thing! So you try to cheat us by undervaluing them! We'll teach you a lesson, young man, you and your cheap Yankee tricks. The penalty for this kind of swindling is confiscation."

They then seized the whole consignment, paying young Jerome his own valuation of $1.50 per clock. When he reported this at home his father was delighted.

"So!" he said. "We sell the entire consignment at a profit without the work of marketing the clocks! That's wonderful!"

And immediately he shipped another consignment. This was also confiscated but by the time the third cargo arrived the officers were convinced.

When Americans became accustomed to clocks in their houses, they began to want watches too. Here, however, was a far more delicate mechanism requiring special skills and an artistry that it seemed impossible to transfer from the trained eyes and hands of the old watchmakers' guilds to a set of machines.

The first watches were made in Germany in the fifteenth century and were, really, small clocks which were usually hung from the belt or girdle. By 1530, however, they were made small enough for the pocket. Because the art of watchmaking had originally been a branch of the jeweler's trade it had always been customary to ennoble the magical little machines by encasing them in gold or silver and ornamenting the cases with precious stones. Originally watches were owned by royalty or nobility, but with the rise of the bourgeoisie in England they came into the hands of all kinds of rich merchants and businessmen. The watch was, however, always a symbol of wealth and the person who was constantly taking out his timepiece did so usually to show off his economic superiority rather than to find out the time. As timekeepers—at least until well into the eighteenth century—watches were of relatively little use.

Watchmakers, like every other kind of immigrant, entered America in colonial times from France, Germany, England and Switzerland and established shops in all the coastal cities, but in general, just as clock manufacture centered in Connecticut, the watch people chose Massachusetts. They never actually "made" a watch until the nineteenth century: their business was in putting together foreign parts, selling imported watches and repairing them. It is probable that no wholly American watch appeared until the 1830's and it was not until the middle of the 1850's that machine-made watch manufacture began.

Aaron Dennison of Boston is credited with being the "father of American watchmaking" although there is probably much to be said for another claimant named Edward Howard. It is difficult to say which of these contributed most to the quantity production of cheap watches, as they were associated in partnership and designed the factory together. The only thing which need concern us about machine watchmaking is that the art was learned by studying gun-making. The fine, precise machine tools which made watches available to every American for a few dollars (and, finally, for a single dollar) were directly descended from the Whitney factory. The Whitney plan had been installed entire in the national armory at Springfield, Massachusetts, and it was there that Aaron Dennison, after his apprentice-ship to a so-called watchmaker, examined the precision work that was being done on rifles. It was only necessary for him to look at this machinery through the wrong end of a mental telescope to visualize a reduction to the point of handling the tiny watch parts. It is said that after his visits to Springfield, he would walk half the night up and down the Boston Common planning lathes, drills, milling ma-chines and many jig and fixture devices.

He even made a model in pasteboard of a watch factory showing all the different departments and, more than fifty years before the Ford Motor Company, planned moving conveyors to transfer work from one set of workmen to an-other.

Dennison and Howard established a plant in Waltham

which became The American Watch Company. In the second year of this company's operation more than twelve thousand watch movements were produced. The accuracy of machine-made watches far exceeded that of the very finest products of the handicraft era. By the time their manufacture got under way the American system had been greatly advanced. Machine tools had not only made the parts of rifles, revolvers and harvesters but also those of sewing machines, precision instruments and fine clocks.

With the sense of the passage of time felt by everyone under the prevalence of time machines, the old easy-going days were over. Lateness at work, school, business appointments was no longer tolerated. In the factories the clock became, to a great extent, the boss. Superintendents and foremen could point to it as the final arbiter when workers were delinquent. As factory work became more exacting, time schedules played an important part in production. Without split-second timing, true mass production could never have been achieved.

When such time-conscious experts as Frederick W. Taylor and Frank Gilbreth introduced what was called "scientific management" into industry, they held stop watches on workers to determine to the fraction of a second how long it took to perform each operation and, finally, each *part* of an operation. By analyzing such time reports, an immense amount of waste motion was eliminated. For example, Taylor found out exactly how long it took many different workers to set up a lathe for a particular job, then the number of seconds for cutting or grinding; again for the readjustment of tools. He could then analyze the motions made by the fast worker and discipline the others to conform. When assembly lines and sub-assemblies came into factories, mathematical exactness of schedules was essential.

The automatic machine for measuring time, therefore, was useful to the march toward mass production in two ways. It introduced new machine tools into the making of precise-fitting interchangeable parts and it made possible the schedules which, later, industrial mathematicians were able to apply to production and assembly lines in the gigantic American factories of today.

CHAPTER NINE

Powered Tools

IN THE SPRING of 1851, Englishmen learned for
the first time of a discovery Yankees had made
some fifty years before and of a practice which Yankees had
followed ever since.

The "Great Exhibition" had just opened in London. It
was a world's fair. All the nations of civilization were represented—with, of course, special emphasis on the British
empire. Nothing on this scale had ever before been attempted. The "Crystal Palace" which housed the show was
eighteen hundred feet long and four hundred feet wide,
entirely constructed of iron and glass.

It was a group of army officers who made the discovery
in a corner of the exhibit of the United States. Like other
visitors, they had smiled when they had come to the American section.

"Well," said one. "It's a young nation after all. You have
to expect a certain amount of empty boasting."

"Right, but where are the exhibits? Surely our American
cousins have more to show than this!"

There were forty thousand square feet of floor space in the American division. It was surmounted by a giant eagle. But what the Americans had to show was mostly in small cases along the walls. There were specimens of newspapers, dishes of wheat and corn, sets of false teeth, a rubber lifeboat and a coffin from which the air had been exhausted so as to keep the body from decomposing. It is scarcely surprising that the Britons were amused by this meager display after all the "eagle-screaming."

One of the officers looked at his catalog and read aloud a paragraph at the head of the American list.

"This," he said, "is impressive."

The expenditure of months or years of labour [the statement read] upon a single article, not to increase its intrinsic value, but solely to augment its cost or its estimation as an object of *virtù*, is not common in the United States. On the contrary, both manual and mechanical labour are applied with direct reference to increasing the number or the quantity of articles suited to the wants of a whole people, and adapted to promote the enjoyment of that moderate competency which prevails among them.

"That seems modest enough," said the lieutenant who had read the passage. "But what does it mean?"

"I assume," said a captain, "that it means they are trying to manufacture enough for everybody."

They moved on and, presently, the captain stopped at a table on which half a dozen rifles were displayed. He picked up one of the guns, balanced it, put it to his shoulder and returned it to the table.

"Nice piece," he said, "but what is there so special about it?"

"Have you read the sign?" the lieutenant said and the captain looked up at the modest legend which hung above the firearms.

ROBBINS & LAWRENCE
Windsor, Vermont
Rifles: the various parts interchangeable.

"Can you explain that?" the lieutenant said.

An American who appeared to be in charge of the exhibit spoke.

"Excuse me," he said, "but what is there that is so hard to understand?"

"How the parts of six rifles can be interchangeable."

The American looked at him with surprise.

"Why," he said, "all our army small arms are made that way. Other mechanisms too. It increases speed and quantity of manufacture."

"So," said the captain. "That would explain that bit in the catalog. Still, I can't quite believe it."

The American then took the rifles apart and gave the British officers the same sort of demonstration Eli Whitney had once given in Washington, picking the parts at random and fitting them together. The officers crowded round watching with amazement as if the Yankee had been a magician.

"Think what that means!" the lieutenant said. "Rifles could be damaged in battle and repaired on the field! Wait till our ordnance people see this! It would save us hundreds of thousands of pounds!"

✦

All through the summer of 1851, army men kept coming to the Robbins and Lawrence exhibit, handling the parts, assembling them themselves and asking questions. Patiently the American explained the methods of manufacture in use at the armories of Springfield, Harper's Ferry and Whitneyville as well as at Windsor, Vermont. He told of the machines, the jigs and the fixtures and the division of labor. And the Englishmen told him, to his surprise, that even in the government's arsenal at Enfield Lock, English guns were still made by individual gunsmiths working at benches in small shops and that every rifle or musket was slightly different from its fellow.

It was two years before the conservative British Army Ordnance Department decided to reform its rifle manufacture along American lines but when, in 1853, the menace of the Crimean war was demanding firearms in quantity, the government went all the way.

To the Small Arms Committee, they appointed the celebrated English engineer, James Nasmyth, inventor of the steam hammer and many engine improvements. Nasmyth knew of the Robbins and Lawrence exhibit and he had seen the Elisha Root machinery at the London factory of Samuel Colt. He had been fascinated by the whole broad pattern these things had disclosed. He wrote of this later in his autobiography:

The United States government . . . had established at Springfield a small-arms factory, where, by the use of machine tools specially designed to execute with the most unerring precision all the details of muskets and rifles, they were enabled to dispense with mere manual dexterity, and to produce arms to any amount.

It was finally determined to improve the musketry and rifle systems of the English army. The government resolved to introduce the American system. . . .

This may have been the first time this phrase was used as no one in the United States ever referred, at that time, to an "American" system.

The committee resolved [Nasmyth continues] to make a personal visit to the United States' factory at Springfield. . . . The United States government acted most liberally in allowing the committee to obtain every information on the subject. . . . The members of the mission returned home enthusiastically delighted with the results of their enquiry. The committee immediately proceeded with the entire remodelling of the Small-arms Factory at Enfield. The workshops were equipped with a complete series of special machine tools, chiefly obtained from the Springfield factory. The United States government also permitted several of their best and most experienced workmen and superintendents to take service under the English government.

Such was the origin of the Enfield rifle.

Thus, more than twenty-five years after his death, Eli Whitney's invention crossed the ocean. It is true that a pattern something like it had been independently designed in England for the making of ship's blocks in the first decade of the nineteenth century, but the wood-working machine tools naturally did not require the precision necessary for gunlocks. At the same time, some very remarkable machine tools had been invented by great English designers like Henry Maudsley—such as the screw-cutting lathe. Yet machines for the quantity production by interchangeable parts of such precise mechanisms as firearms, simply did not exist, at the time, outside the United States.

Nasmyth, in his brief autobiography, does not go fully into detail about his committee's explorations and discoveries in the United States but there are American records which tell most of the surprising story. The committee did get information about the gun-making machinery at Springfield but the machinery itself was supplied by the companies which had supplied Springfield. The chief of these was the very one which had modestly exhibited its interchangeable rifles at the London exhibition in 1851: Robbins and Lawrence of Windsor, Vermont. The committee's contract with this firm covered some hundred and fifty machines especially built to make the Enfield rifle as well as many jigs and fixtures. The list included such advanced tools as multiple-spindle drilling machines and every sort of milling machine including the universal miller. The other company which helped equip the British factory was the Ames Company of Chicopee Falls, Massachusetts, the enterprising mill town where our friend Elisha Root got his early mechanical training. It was a small world, this early community of the American system!

But how, in these early years, with the scarcity of skilled labor, the continual lure of the western lands, the necessity of importing the tool steel from abroad, the extreme transportation difficulties, the bitter winters freezing the water power, the prevailing ignorance of science, had tools been developed which amazed even the experts from highly civilized England which had every means the Yankees lacked?

The saga of Amercian machine tools is one of the most

nearly incredible of all our true legends: its records of the quiet, steady perseverance, the tough courage and the penetrating intuition of a mere handful of creative geniuses in the valley of the Connecticut River give the final testimony to the indomitable industrial impulse which has brought us at last to world leadership.

The records have been hard to find. The early inventors did not even make finished drawings of their machines. For the patents, wooden models and descriptions in legal language sufficed. The men were silent workers, not given to keeping diaries or even writing letters. They had neither time nor money for formal education. Some of the shop men who became giants of the saga worked for years for a hundred dollars a year and board. Materials were carried by sledges in the winter; ox-teams or pack horses in other seasons.

To understand the impulses which kept these men going, we must go back to some early origins and then trace their connection with frontier influences. As in most of our history the frontiers—backwoods and primitive farming areas —played the largest part in the making of the industrial stories.

We think of the frontier as being in the West. There was a time, however, in the colonial period, when it ran through New England. Frontier farms were always "self-sufficient" or "subsistence" farms, which meant that everything the farmer and his family needed was grown or made at home. Visits to the remote town were rarely necessary as only a few items such as salt, refined sugar and books had to be bought. There were, however, two or three needs requiring outside help: the milling of grain into meal or flour and the forging of iron. On the frontiers, therefore, within reach of every farmer, was a grist-mill using either horse or water power, and a blacksmith's shop. The self-sufficient farm and the blacksmith shop between them formed the cradle of Yankee ingenuity.

In New England, winters were long. In the frozen time no farming was possible and farmers had to find other means of occupying themselves. Together with the blacksmiths they made every sort of thing in their spare time: guns, clocks, nails, tinware, combs and buttons, ox-yokes, sleighs, even musical instruments. Eventually they accumulated more of these things than they needed and sold them. Some farmers and blacksmiths turned peddler and, as we have seen, toured the South with pack-horses or little wagons. As soon as peddling became popular and profitable, machine shops and, finally, factories became necessary to keep the peddlers supplied. Finally, after the Revolution, as the frontiers started moving westward, peddling on roads and boats grew into a large organized business, and throughout the northeast manufacture began to supplant farming.

In many parts of the frontier, hunting was an essential occupation. Rifles were therefore designed and made in the Pennsylvania backwoods and by the time of the Revolution this weapon had found its way all along the wilderness line to Vermont and it was Washington's organization of these frontier riflemen which was largely responsible for American victory in the war. This necessitated gunshops and many a blacksmith turned gunsmith, so here again was a need for ingenuity. Yet as the West opened, men left the gunshops too so each mechanic who remained had to reproduce himself, so to speak: to make himself into ten, twenty or a hundred mechanics. So there must have been rejoicing in the valley of the Connecticut from Windsor, Vermont, to Hartford when, in New Haven, Eli Whitney designed and, in Middletown, Simeon North developed, the system of interchangeable manufacture. (Both these men, incidentally, as well as Sam Colt, Elisha Root, Cyrus McCormick and Jerome had begun life on subsistence farms.)

To follow all the movement from farm to shop to factory in the formative period of American industry let us follow the career of one young man, the results of whose work we met in London at the beginning of this chapter.

Richard Smith Lawrence left Vermont at two to grow up on his father's farm in Watertown, N. Y. Farming was bad there and the boy spent more and more of his time in the village blacksmith shop. Finally he was getting jobs with mechanics and gunsmiths in the neighborhood, but a jinx of bad luck seemed to follow him for every time he had a foot on a new rung of the ladder, climbing to success, the shop he was in burned to the ground and Lawrence was, as he expressed it in a later account of his life, "left out in the cold." He persisted, however, and as he, like everyone else in that country, was a hunter, he learned a good deal about backwoods rifles. He kept his own gun in repair and fixed those of his non-mechanical neighbors.

When his father died there was no further reason for Richard to stay on the farm so by canal boat and on foot he traveled to Vermont and sought out some of his relatives who lived near Windsor. In particular, there was a Doctor Story, an uncle who offered to board him. Perhaps his reason for staying with this uncle was the fact that Story's brother, Asa, was a gunsmith.

The doctor owned two hunting pieces: a "turkey rifle" made by his brother and an old Pennsylvania rifle with a four-foot barrel and "all rusty." It might have been used in the Revolution by Green Mountain boys—as so many of these fine, accurate firearms had been. Richard ignored the good turkey rifle and concentrated his attention on the rusty one.

"I can repair this, uncle," he said. "And I would like to put a peep sight on it."

The doctor had never seen a peep sight and when Richard described it he was interested. But he said:

"No, I don't dare trust you with it. It was one of the best rifles I ever had and I've killed many a deer with it. I'm afraid you'll spoil it."

Richard was not one to be put off with this kind of answer. He was sure of himself and he said so. How often he said so, he does not tell us but he wrote:

After a while he consented to let me make the trial and went over with me to his brother's shop and obtained his consent to let me use his shop and tools. I went to work, took the gun all apart, leaded out the barrel, forged out the sight, finished it and put it on the gun. His brother watched me all day. He had never seen a peep sight and a mere boy handling tools and forging out work as I did was a little astonishing to him.

When the doctor saw the repaired rifle he was delighted and made an appointment for the next day to try it out. It was then that Richard had a shock which, for a moment, almost made him believe the jinx had followed him to Windsor.

For the trial the doctor picked out a maple tree which had a three-quarter-inch auger hole in it made for a sap spout at sugaring-off time. He then paced off twelve rods (66 yards). He said that the auger hole would be the target.

I found a good rest, [Richard wrote] lay down on the ground and fired. The Doct. tended target. Could find no ball hole. Said I had missed the tree. I fired again—no ball hole could be found. Doct. came up to me and said I had spoiled his Rifle. Before my repairs he could kill a chicken every time at 12 rods. I said "Uncle, I am very sorry, but I will make the gun all right before I leave it." He said he would not consent to my doing anything more. . . . I said that as the gun was loaded would take one more shot and see if I could not hit the tree. After the third shot I went up to the tree to investigate, and all of the three balls which I had fired were found in the auger hole. The Doct. was astonished—dumbfounded. Said he had never heard of such shooting. We spent half the night talking about guns. . . .

Windsor on the Connecticut River under Mount Ascutney was, when Richard Lawrence came to it in 1838, already a manufacturing town. There was plenty of fine water power to attract mechanics. Farmers, tired of the short seasons in the mountainous country, had drifted there and gone into its shops and forges. Its gunshops had made and repaired Revolutionary rifles. Iron had been found in the bogs and smelted. A number of inventions had been made by ma-

chine-minded runaways from the farms: an efficient rotary
pump, a machine for automatically marking the scale on a
ruler or square; a machine for ruling lines on paper and
several rifle improvements including the "under-hammer"
which placed the hammer below the barrel so that it would
not interfere with the sighting—a curiosity much prized
today by collectors. In the 1830's, one of Asa Story's assistant
gunsmiths, Nicanor Kendall, had started a gun factory
where he made rifles in quantity on the Whitney system
and sent many of them to Texas for its war of liberation in
Mexico in 1836.

This factory operated in a peculiar fashion. It stood next
door to the Windsor prison. In his machine shops, Kendall
used both convict and free labor. The prisoners were escorted
by a guard from their cells to the machines they were to
tend: after working through the day they were taken back
and locked up. It was one of the strangest labor arrange-
ments in American industrial history. Apparently it worked.
The prisoners were grateful to Kendall for giving them an
interesting occupation and several expressions of their grati-
tude are on record!

It was to the Kendall factory that Doctor Story took Richard Lawrence the day after the trial of the old rifle. To
Kendall's superintendent, the doctor told the story of the
repaired rifle with which, using his peep sight, the boy had
fired three successive shots squarely into the sap hole of a
maple twelve rods away, and Lawrence was hired on the
spot.

His work there, in addition to machine work, included
bookkeeping and escorting the convict workmen to and

from their cells. While he was at the books he practiced penmanship and some of the sheets on which he worked were afterward found. In a flourishing hand he had written and repeated the words "R. S. Lawrence, Superintendent" —showing the beginnings in the twenty-one-year-old mind of that ambition which was to make him one of the key figures in the story of American machine tools.

In six years, Lawrence had become Kendall's partner in a new firm called Robbins, Kendall and Lawrence and this shortly became the Robbins and Lawrence Company so that at a little over thirty, the "unlucky" farm lad had become the engineering head of the institution which, in 1851, was to make the American system of interchangeable-parts manufacture famous overseas. It is interesting to note that in the years immediately preceding the London show, Robbins and Lawrence received a contract from the United States government for ten thousand army rifles; that in order to fill this they advertised for workers and got, we are told, "many experts from the shops of Eli Whitney . . . and the National Armories at Springfield and Harper's Ferry," in all of which the Whitney system had been installed entire.

Lawrence concentrated on machine tools, many of which he invented. Among them were machines for barrel-drilling and rifling as well as milling machines. It was customary in the 1850's for rifle manufacturers to make their own machines or powered tools. Yet already there were signs that the manufacture of "machines to make machines" would soon become an industry of its own. A reason for this was that there was another sort of interchangeability in tool-making. As powered tool-making became more and more standardized it was evident that the *machines that made the machines that made the machines* were all much alike. In short, once you had mastered a few basic tool principles, you could make almost anything. So the shops which made drills for gun barrels could also make drills for the parts of sewing machines: the so-called "millers," which cut, or grinders, which finished the pieces of a rifle lock, were no different, basically, from those which worked on the forgings or castings that went into a steam engine. Let us take a look, then, at what some of these machines were and without going into too much technical detail, their many uses will be apparent.

At thirteen, Thomas Blanchard, son of a Massachusetts "self-sufficient farmer," invented a machine for paring apples. There may have been no connection in his mind between this and his later achievement, but the invention of his thirty-fourth year—for which he will be forever celebrated—was a machine for paring the wooden stocks of firearms until they assumed the correct shape. This was an operation which, until 1820, notwithstanding all the Whitney automatic machinery, had always been performed by hand. Stocks were "whittled." No lathe was capable of handling so irregular a shape. Blanchard's "stocking lathe" did the job by means of a friction wheel and a cutting wheel attached to the same shaft. As the friction wheel followed the curves of a finished stock—used as a pattern—the cutting wheel moved in and out of the piece of wood to be cut, reproducing every contour of the pattern. When his lathe was built, Blanchard found that it would copy any desired shape exactly. It therefore became useful not only for making gun stocks but also for shoe lasts, hat blocks, wheel spokes and many other things. He improved it with a kind of pantograph attachment so that it would reproduce articles in reduced or enlarged sizes.

Working in the Springfield Armory under the constant inspiration of the Whitney system, Blanchard invented many other automatic gun-making machines and, being an extremely versatile person, he later built a steam automobile and a steamboat designed to run upstream through rapids.

The oldest and most fundamental machine tool is the lathe. In the ancient lathe, a chunk of wood was spun on a spindle while a cutting tool was held against it by the hand.

The English engineer, Henry Maudslay, gave to the lathe its first great improvement, the slide rest—a device holding the tool in a clamp. The slide rest was threaded into a long screw. As a crank was turned, the screw moved the rest slowly in a groove and the tool was pressed into the revolving piece of material. Stops controlled the exact depth of the cut. Maudslay also adapted the lathe to metal working.

The perfected lathe could use a large number of tools but when tools were changed the lathe had to be stopped while the old tool was taken out and the new one clamped in. The first great American contribution to lathe invention was the "turret lathe." Here the slide rest was replaced by a revolving turret into which all the tools necessary for a given phase of manufacture were clamped beforehand. Thus, when one operation was finished, it was only necessary to give a slight turn to the turret to bring a new tool into play. The turret lathe was invented in 1845 by Stephen Fitch; a quarter century later Christopher Spencer made it automatic so that it could perform a whole series of operations with no one to attend it.

From the time of Eli Whitney's early musket-making, some form of milling machine was in use in metal work. Whitney himself seems to have built the first one. The simplest form of a milling machine chips or cuts metal with a rapidly revolving sharp-toothed wheel. By moving the wheel over a surface an effect like planing is produced: if it is held at a certain point it makes a cut like that of a chisel. Even Whitney's crude powered tool had automatic stops so that the cutting wheel would cease at the proper depth, but as time went on the controls multiplied and the jobs a "miller" could perform greatly increased. It was brought to a high point when Fredecick W. Howe, Richard Lawrence's right-hand man at the Robbins and Lawrence Company's factory, invented the "universal milling machine." This versatile tool could cut, not only at right angles but at every angle; it could, indeed, do practically everything a hand tool could do and much more besides, precisely and automatically. It was this machine which did most of the work on the rifles Robbins and Lawrence exhibited in London in 1851. The majority of the machine tools used in today's factories are adaptations of the milling machine.

These were the main machine tools. There were countless others but most of them were adaptations of principles established by Lawrence, Blanchard, Fitch, Howe or by such great English tool builders as Henry Maudslay. But in comparing the inventions of Americans and Englishmen we shall generally find that the English emphasis is on precision; the American on speed.

After 1850 "mechanics" became engineers: from then on, precision increased, work became more and more specialized, elaborate mathematical calculations were applied, working drawings and, later, blueprints were many and exact, separately covering every tiniest part of every machine. When individual electric motors replaced the belting and shafts of the old water- or steam-powered plants the whole aspect of the factory changed and the way was open for the full development of mass production as we see it in the great automotive factories of today.

Perhaps the most fascinating thing about the machine-tool story in America is the fact that those who began it seem almost to have been members of a family. The area in which they worked was so limited: in all of it there was a common climate, common occupations—farm, smithy, primitive gunshop—and the great common incentive to speed up and multiply production so that the few could supply the many. Most of these men knew each other. Nearly all of them seem to have worked their apprenticeships out in the same places: Windsor, Hartford, Chicopee Falls, New Haven, Waterbury. Their first work was on the same few devices: first textile machinery, then guns and axes, then reapers, perhaps sewing machines or timepieces. When we study the genealogy of the tremendous tool-making companies of today—Pratt and Whitney, Brown and Sharpe, Stanley and dozens of others—we can nearly always trace the pedigrees back to the shops described in this chapter in cold, snow-bound, rugged communities in the New England river valleys amid the dying subsistence farms.

CHAPTER TEN

Clothing and Shoes

W HEN I was a youngster," wrote Oliver Johnson in his reminiscences of pioneer farming
in Indiana, "all our clothin was linen. We didn't have any
sheep for several years on account of the wolves. Besides, the
woods was so full of burrs, briers and brush that the wool
would a been ruined."

He goes on in his colloquial manner to tell of the difficulties of making linen which seemed to worry no one
except those who wore it in the bitter winters. Even they—
the children at least—complained little: complaint, after
all, would not have helped. "If you got too cold," Johnson
wrote, "you put on two shirts and two pair of britches—that
as if you had em."

Of all the textiles, linen involved most processes before
the thread was ready for the loom. The flax was pulled up
by the roots, dried and spread on the ground in the autumn
so that the fall rains would rot the core of the stalks, leaving
the outside fiber firm. The stalks were then bound up in
bundles and laid away till cold weather made them brittle.

They were then run through a hand breaker which broke the stalks into pieces of the right length.

Then [explained Johnson] it was scotched or swingled by graspin a bundle in one hand and layin it across a solid board. With a wooden knife in the other hand it was whipped and beaten until all the dry heart of the stalk fell out leavin only the outside fiber.

Hackles—boards "with a lot of sharp spikes stickin up"— pulled off seeds and roots and left "fine silky strands. The bunch of them was wound around a distaff and the flax was ready for spinnin."

These things were done by the men on the farm; the women took over the spinning and weaving of the linen and the cutting and sewing of clothing for the entire family as well as towels, tablecloths and sheets. Adding these jobs to cooking, preserving, washing, soap- and candle-making and the care of the younger children, it is hardly surprising that the pioneer farm woman became a drudge with no time but the strictly kept Sabbath for rest or thought or reading. It is interesting to compare the lives of these folk with the activity of a housewife in the 1950's who sews only repairs and works in a push-button kitchen in which a dozen mechanical servants wash, dry, cook, freeze, and supply the light and heat. If the ghost of Mr. Johnson's mother could meet one of today's smartly and warmly dressed women on her way out of the supermarket wheeling a wire "baby carriage" full of pre-cooked food, drive home with her to the stream-lined kitchen and tell her on the way a few stories of Indiana a century and a quarter ago, it would probably surprise her. Unfortunately, today's Americans, though they may have learned much about elections and political parties of the period, have been told little of home life on the frontiers in the infancy of mass production.

Pap made all the shoes [Johnson went on] for our big family. He would work on shoes only of evenins. They was for winter wear. In the summer most everybody went barefoot, especially the women and children. . . . In the fall Pap would go to town and buy or trade for a half side of sole leather and a half side of upper leather. Mother's and his shoes was always made first, then shoes for the girls. Us boys come last. Sometimes . . . it would be up toward Christmas before I got any shoes. . . .

On frosty mornins in the fall we would heat a clapboard before the fireplace until it was almost charred, stick it under our arm and run through the frost until our feet began to sting. Then we threw the clapboard on the ground, stood on it until our feet warmed, grab it up and make another run. . . .

On the frontiers of the Middle West, conditions more or less like this lasted until the Civil War. The first relief for the women came when peddlers brought cloth made by machine in the eastern textile mills to replace the homespun, though even then cotton underwear, shirts and all women's garments had to be cut and hand-sewed at home. Manufactured shoes—largely hand-made but produced in quantity by the highly organized Massachusetts industry—came next; "Pap" was able to abandon his cobbler's bench in the evenings and there were fewer chilblains. These things varied, of course, in different parts of the country. Where transportation was easy along the interior waterways, towns grew up close behind the farms and there all the industrial products of the East were available. A day's journey or less might put a farmer in touch with a shoe store, a dry goods store and a tailor, but little ready-made clothing of any kind was for sale before the mid-century and what there was was of such bad quality that self-respecting farmers would have none of it. Work clothes were made at home until well after the Civil War out of bought denim and other coarse materials and the men's "Sunday best" was made to order by itinerant or village tailors.

The women do not seem to have been aware of the terrible burdens of their lives until they were relieved of them. They simply accepted them as part of their fate. "Rest" was something which belonged in the next world; the word appears with great frequency in the Calvinist hymns. But when the news came that there was, truly, a promise of relief here on earth, women rose up everywhere in protest against their drudgery and with vigorous organization and eloquent oratory promoted every sort of emancipation movement including, eventually, the demand for a vote. What came to be known as "feminism" in America, therefore, may be traced directly to the production of the sewing machine.

We usually think of this great invention as being useful mainly in the home. That is because the advertising we see —whether it is in Bagdad, Tai Pei, Alaska or a Borneo jungle; in New York, Chilicothe, Las Vegas or Portland— is always of the convenient little machine operated by the lady of the house, hut or igloo. There is hardly a hamlet so small or so remote in all the world in which at least one sewing machine cannot be found and we think of it as lightening the labor of housewives of every race and color. This was not, however, the most important function of the sewing machine. It achieved its peak of power when it was adapted to the factory. Its greatest saving of labor came in the mass production of clothes and shoes. The total emancipation of woman did not arrive because she was able to sew her own and her husband's clothes on a machine instead of by hand. It became possible only when she, her husband and her children could go to stores and buy everything they wore *ready made*.

The curious thing was that when the machine was first invented it was thought to be a menace to the women: presumably it would take the bread out of the mouths of those who sewed for a living! Thus the French inventor, Barthélemy Thimonnier, who as early as 1831 had built eighty machines which were used to make army uniforms, had nearly all of them destroyed by a mob, and the American, Walter Hunt (inventor of the safety pin), who produced a sewing machine in 1834 seems to have been afraid to patent or exploit it for the same reason. Actually, the sewing machine, when it became practical, gave employment to more women than any invention made up to that time.

The first truly practical machine was the product of several brilliant and persistent American minds. Elias Howe, Jr., Isaac Singer, Allen Wilson, James Gibbs and William Grover all contributed something and the machine as we know it embodies some fraction of all their thought. To us it is so commonplace that we cannot easily see why, in the beginning, it was so exceedingly difficult to invent. If, however, we will imagine that we have never seen any kind of sewing but that done by a needle held in the hand, inserted in the cloth, drawn back, inserted again and the whole operation repeated through the long seam, we shall be in the position of the men who made this precious gift to society.

A frail boy, born lame, Elias Howe could not cope with the heavy work on his father's Massachusetts farm. Elias, Senior, however, owned a grist-mill and a saw-mill and these provided occupation for the lad who was fascinated by machinery. At sixteen he went to Lowell which was already, in 1835, the principal textile mill town in the country and there was apprenticed to a manufacturer of mill machinery. The understanding of looms Howe gained in these years was the basis of his invention.

His next job was with an instrument maker in Boston, an eccentric character named Ari Davis. In Davis' machine shop, Harvard professors used to spend many hours explaining the delicate scientific equipment they needed and often inventors or men who hoped to be inventors would drop in to talk. Davis must have been a stimulating person. Usually in the life of every creative mechanician, there is someone like Davis who invents nothing himself but inspires others. One day, during a discussion among a number of these visitors in the shop, someone said,

"Why don't you make a sewing machine?"

"That," said his friend, "is impossible. Knitting machines and looms, yes, but no machine can sew."

"Nonsense," Ari Davis interrupted, "I can make a sewing machine myself."

"All right, you do it, Davis," the first speaker said, "and I'll guarantee you an independent fortune."

None of them saw the pale, thin, curly-haired lad in the back of the shop. But Elias Howe had stopped his watch-maker's lathe to listen. Silently he stared at the man who had been willing to back Davis. He had a prosperous look about him. There must be many wealthy capitalists, Howe thought, who would support such a venture and an independent fortune was the thing this young man who had grown up in poverty wanted more than anything else. So the memory of the conversation in the shop remained in his mind and kept plaguing him and keeping him awake. Davis forgot it immediately and apparently Howe did not remind him. Perhaps he did not want to share either the fortune or the credit. Inventors, as a rule, are jealous folk.

If Howe had not married the following year, he too might have forgotten. When, however, three children arrived in rapid succession, his wife spent much of her time sewing clothes for them. It must have exasperated her sometimes to see her young husband who was earning only nine dollars a week as a journeyman machinist sit hour after hour watching her as she sewed when he might have been out working to keep the little family fed and clothed. She could hardly have known that his intense mental activity during this apparent idleness would end in taking the needle forever out of the hands of tired mothers like herself.

But how to make a machine go through the complicated motions of his Elizabeth's fingers? In the months before Howe's idea came to him, he learned what many inventors have had to learn before him, that he must purge from his mind every memory of hand work before he could attempt to make wheels, cranks and levers accomplish the same result. Many an inventor has gone mad trying to make mechanical devices follow the motions of the human body. John Fitch wasted precious time and money trying to make a steam engine pull the oars of a boat before the idea of the paddle wheel occurred to him.

The revolutionary sewing-machine idea was to put the eye of the needle in its point instead of in its head. The needle could then carry the thread through the cloth without passing wholly through it itself. Entering the cloth at right angles to it instead of obliquely as in hand sewing, it could form a loop of thread on the farther side. Seeing this loop on his experimental machine, Howe remembered the loom and knew that a shuttle carrying another thread could be made to pass through the loop so that when the needle moved back again a lock stitch would be formed by the two threads.

By the spring of 1845, six years after he had listened to the dialogue in Davis' shop, Howe had a machine that would sew a seam. It is an odd-looking device which we may see today in the National Museum at Washington. The needle moves in a horizontal plane; the cloth is held vertically. Howe interested a capitalist sufficiently to get money for a model (then required by the Patent Office) and obtained a patent. There then occurred one of the most astonishing, comic and at the same time tragically disheartening series of events in the history of invention.

Howe exhibited his machine, trying to get orders. People

crowded in to see the thing sew; there were contests between the machine and hand sewers with rules and umpires, and the machine, crude as it was, won. But all this was regarded as a kind of circus trick! Spectators laughed and applauded and told each other about the magic toy. But no one took it seriously for a moment. It was fun but what was it for? You could hardly expect professional tailors—serious working men and women—to use a gadget like that!

Apparently from the first Howe thought of the machine as being used by tailoring establishments rather than in the home. Disgusted at last with the attitude he encountered, he took his machine to England and there it instantly attracted the attention of a corset maker. We cannot go into the tribulations of the inventor, his unhappy wife and his loyal brother Amasa when the Englishman swindled Elias unmercifully, but the point is that the first use to which a sewing machine was put was in a factory. For us, in this story of production, the sewing machine occupies a key position for it performed a double function. It made possible the mass production of clothing and shoes and, especially when it was made in a light, convenient form for the home, it became itself mass-produced, requiring a high development of the American system in the manufacture of extremely precise small moving parts.

Isaac Merrit Singer was the pioneer in this phase. Today the company he founded in the 1850's makes every kind of manufacturing machine for cloth, leather and other materials but Singer's greatest success in the early years came from sales of the home machines.

Singer was the opposite of Howe. His early career was wild and roving, moving from place to place, holding jobs for only a short time, temperamental, and getting into frequent trouble. He had an iron constitution and a stubborn capacity for hard work, often staying up all night to advance his project. His career began also in a Boston machine shop.

By 1850 a number of experimenters had tried their hand at this invention. A machine was brought into the shop where Singer worked for repairs. His boss asked Singer what he thought of it and, though he had never seen a sewing machine before, he gave an instantaneous criticism. By seeing a machine which was all wrong, by analyzing its defects and correcting them, Singer made his great contribution to the art. It may seem a backhanded method of invention but it ended in fabulous success.

Independently of Howe, he thought of the eye at the point end of the needle. He made it move vertically, however. He added what he called the "yielding presser foot" to hold the cloth in position and the "continuous wheel feed" which kept the cloth moving as the needle sewed—eliminating the necessity of pushing it with the hand. He made his lock stitch with a shuttle as Howe had done.

The Singer story from then on is a strange one. The success of the machine and of the fabulous company which made it had the oddest basis of any such triumph in American history. It came from a lawsuit which Singer lost and which cost him fifteen thousand dollars early in his career.

It did not take Elias Howe long to discover that Singer was selling machines which contained at least two of his patented inventions, the eye-pointed needle and the lock-stitch-forming shuttle. He therefore brought suit for infringement. To fight this, Singer engaged a brilliant lawyer, Edward Clark, who gave his services in exchange for an interest in the company. Though Howe won the suit, Clark's partnership in the Singer Company resulting from it guaranteed the company's success. Clark was an able lawyer, but as a businessman and financier he was a genius. However fine Singer's technical contributions had been—and there is hardly a doubt that, in the middle 1850's his machine led the field—it was Clark and the members of the Clark family who followed him who created one of the great industrial organizations of the world. The effect of the Singer institution on international society is almost incalculable. In America it advanced interchangeable manufacture to the point where the bicycle and the automobile became possible.

Elias Howe received ample reward for his efforts. Controlling the basic patents, every sewing-machine manufacturer was obliged to buy a license from Howe. Thus, although his machines were never the equal of those made by Singer, Wheeler and Wilson, Grover and Baker or Willcox and Gibbs the royalties all of them paid him made him a millionaire. Eventually, the leading manufacturers got together, pooled their patents and formed a "combination" or trust so that, in the 1860's we find various patents appearing on all the machines just as, today, such things as fluid drives, automatic chokes and hydraulic brakes are shared by all the leading motor car manufacturers.

The 1860's were terrible years in the history of the United States. In them we fought our most destructive war and came close to dissolution. The South was plunged into a devastation and a distress from which recovery took some thirty years. Yet in the North, in spite of military defeats and passions which tore families apart, prosperity, on the whole, increased.

The Civil War gave a great boost to industries of all sorts. The ready-made clothing trade took its first satisfactory start from the establishments which made soldiers' uniforms. It was this manufacture which established and standardized sizes. The many measurements of soldiers which the government accumulated furnished data for averages on which civilian clothing was based. Juggling these figures the clothing industrialist could reduce them to a set of sizes such as "36" or "42" in men's clothing. It was found that a man with a certain chest size would, on the average, have other dimensions such as sleeve length, trouser length and waist measurement to conform. The establishment of standardized sizes involved a truly scientific handling of statistics and it was years before factory-made clothes could approach the custom products in fit. By that time, special sizes had also been designed for men who departed from the averages and these were called "long," "short," "stout," "short stout," "portly," "forward," "young stout," "stalwart," "corpulent," and other names.

At first, after the machine came, clothes were cut by the manufacturer and "farmed out" to people who either owned machines or were lent them by the manufacturer. This caused a dangerous practice known as "sweating." Machine work was done by an entire family on parts of a suit cut by a "master tailor" or manufacturing clothier. As these people were paid starvation wages they lived in crowded and unsanitary homes and for some twenty years, while this sinister exploitation went on, infectious diseases were (or were thought to be) carried by the clothes. As other machines—cutters, buttonhole makers, et cetera—were invented it was found more convenient and economical to make garments in a factory on something resembling assembly lines. Sweating was also fought vigorously by unionized garment workers and, eventually, was abolished. Clothing factories today are models of cleanliness and efficiency and, though they have driven most custom tailors out of business, they have made up for it in benefit to society as a whole.

Cutting machines, which cut sixteen thicknesses of cloth at once, were operated by knives which moved through slots in a table. The slots were laid out by patterns so that the knives cutting out the makings of a pair of pants, for example, would follow precisely the curves of the design for each piece. These machines reduced the time necessary to cut a hundred pairs of pants from sixteen hours and forty minutes by the old hand shears to one hour and thirty-four minutes, or a hundred vests from about seventeen hours to less than three hours. Buttonhole cutting on a hundred coats went from three hours and twenty minutes by hand to seventeen and a half minutes by machine.

Sewing machines were operated mainly by girls. It was this giving of jobs to women who had never worked before which provided them with an entirely new status and greatly helped the movement toward "emancipation" and suffrage. As soon as women were capable of going out and earning their own living they were no longer "slaves" to their husbands and fathers as in the days of their confining household drudgery.

The impetus given to the manufacture of clothing by the Civil War was, however, far less revolutionary than that which occurred in shoemaking. For here, starting with the sewing machine, the entire business became mechanized as a result of government orders for soldiers' boots and shoes.

From early times American shoemaking, though not using many machines, had been "industrialized." In Lynn and Brockton in Massachusetts, the first shoe centers, there was what was known as "cottage manufacture." Cut leather was farmed out to individuals who sewed it by hand. Unlike other domestic industries, however, these shoemakers all lived in one place in a row of cottages so long and with such rigid standardization that visitors from England such as Harriet Martineau could hardly believe their eyes when they first saw such astonishing establishments. But, centralized as these people were, it was far less difficult to make the transition to factories than with the clothiers.

With the machines, factories were inevitable. The war contracts provided the capital to erect the buildings, to speed the invention of difficult shoemaking machinery and to build and install the machines. The war necessity probably hastened the use of shoe machinery by about thirty years.

Most of the machines were invented by Lyman Blake and Charles Goodyear, Jr., but the capitalist and promoter, Gordon McKay, put his trade-mark on the machines and Blake and Goodyear were largely forgotten. It was McKay's enterprise, however, his drive and his business resources that made it possible to fill government contracts of unheard of size. One contract, for instance, called for 800,000 pairs of army shoes and we may imagine what would have happened to such an order under the old hand-stitching system.

With Blake's adaptation of the sewing machine each worker produced a hundred times as much as he had done working by hand. By the end of the war sole leather which had been hand hammered was rolled by machine; machines also took over the hand operations of splitting upper leather, forming the soles, stitching the upper leather and binding the edges, sewing the uppers to the soles and forming and attaching the heels. Every one of these had previously been a slow, laborious hand operation.

The sewing machine was the first real luxury which entered the home as a result of the American system. By 1870 half a million machines were produced every year. Singer and Clark were pioneers in installment selling. They took more of a chance than McCormick, who sold his harvester for a small down payment, because McCormick was reasonably sure the harvester would make money for the farmer. Whether the sewing machine in the home would actually earn money or would simply make the family's clothing was problematical. Furthermore, the Singers were dealing not with the proverbially honest farmers but with city dwellers who were supposed to have less scrupulous standards. Yet the American people everywhere proved proud of being able to pay the debts they had incurred in this great step toward social democracy.

From here on, we shall find that machines which make machines can easily be adapted to kindred products. Thus we find firearms establishments taking on the manufacture of sewing machines and, when they came, typewriters; later both these industries went in for the manufacture of bicycles and, finally, automobiles. In the 1880's and '90's when the country was covered with a network of railroads; when steam power made its greatest advance and electric power was coming in, the whole American complex became tighter, smoother, faster-moving. Businesses were combining in mergers and trusts, finance had become a kind of magic, management had become scientific, enormous quantities of accounting and paper work were done by armies of "white-collar" workers—clerks, bookkeepers, statisticians—and it was becoming evident that the business machine would have to follow the typewriter in order to keep businessmen abreast of the details of the new efficiency.

It was in this time that the frontier stopped moving. In 1850, it had leapfrogged across the Great Plains to California under the impetus of the gold discovery; in the next thirty years there were two frontiers, one moving as it had always moved from east to west, the other rushing from west to east, to fill up the empty spaces which had been skipped. The first great rail span from the Atlantic to the Pacific was completed in 1869. From then on, the wilderness disappeared with amazing speed. By the 1880's the two frontiers had met, the Great Plains had been settled except for deserts and "bad lands" and they had been traversed by railroads. There was nowhere else to go. The continent had been conquered.

CHAPTER ELEVEN

Machines for
Fun and Freedom

THE HARD FIGHT to redeem the wilderness across the continent kept Americans so busy during our formative years that little time or energy was left for playing. Visitors from abroad commented on the fact that the people here seldom relaxed; that they were always intensely concentrated on some project, and that the leisure for recreation so abundantly enjoyed in Europe scarcely existed in the United States. This amused and puzzled travelers from older, long-settled countries. To us as we consider the strenuous necessities of hunting, clearing, plowing, farming, the long, slow travel with pack-horses or ox-drawn wagons over Indian and buffalo trails and, back in the older eastern centers, the demands for industry and trade, it is understandable that even our beloved national game, baseball, was not organized until the mid-nineteenth century.

Organized sports began, quite naturally, in the more thickly populated and more settled East. There the popularity of baseball spread quickly. In the 1850's, some fifty clubs formed the National Association of Base Ball Players.

The champion team, Dodger fans are glad to know, was a Brooklyn outfit known as the "Excelsiors" and they made a tour of the eastern states giving exhibition games to an attendance which ran as high as 15,000. Until 1869, however, when the all-professional Cincinnati Red Stockings appeared, baseball was largely an amateur sport.

Football did not arrive until the 1870's when Harvard and Yale drew up a set of rules for an adaptation of the English Rugby. From then until the end of the century the interest in sports grew with feverish intensity: rowing, hockey, tennis, golf and the ancient track and field activities were imported; basketball was invented in 1891 in Springfield, Massachusetts, and all these had their national associations and growing bodies of fans. They all began as "gentlemen's games" in the hands of well-to-do members of a leisure class but most of them, like everything else in America, were soon democratized.

When the sports became a national craze, competition grew so hot and standards of performances became so high that, although the number of fans required vast bleachers and stadiums, only a select few could take part. Before the turn of the century, gate receipts had already become a factor in athletic events at the colleges and inducements were being offered to boys whose muscles were more powerful than their minds.

A writer in a popular magazine in 1896 comments on this "evil" by way of introducing a wonderful new invention which was bringing health and happiness to millions of Americans:

One often hears an objection to the athletic enthusiasms of our colleges on the ground that fierce competition and semi-professionalism in games tend to bring forward only the phenomenally muscular and robust men, leaving the rank and file of students, who have most need of physical training, to shift for themselves, and indeed to actually discourage them from outdoor games by setting standards so impossible for them to attain. The absolute physical inability to shine in the fiercer athletic sports has certainly resigned many an anaemic youth to a steady and unremitting grind at his books where a biceps under the normal need prove no bar to the capture of honors. . . . If this be true of the colleges, it is a still more decided evil in business life . . . where the approval and pleasures to be won by physical prowess are even less easy of attainment. . . .

The article goes on to say that now, however, these handicaps to the more abundant life are forever a thing of the past. Since 1890 something has arrived among us which gives every man, woman and child in the country a chance for happy outdoor exercise and to develop muscles to his heart's content! It provides competition, skill, the highest co-ordination and a fine sense of balance—not to mention a great deal of sweat and aching calves. And *anyone* can learn to handle it!

Everything the article said was true except its implication that this blessing's "firm hold on the public" was a lasting matter.

To us, today, the bicycle is a useful toy. Newsboys, messengers and other young workers still use it to ply their trade. But we associate it with children or, at least, with those too young to qualify for a driver's license. But we have forgotten that, in its brief career, the bicycle exerted a most powerful effect upon American history. By starting the movement for hard, smooth roads it literally paved the way for the automobile. And, both physically and psychologically, it was the true parent of the motor car.

It was natural for bicycling to begin in Europe where the roads were better. In no aspect of civilization was the United States so far behind as in roads. There were several good reasons for this. We lacked the European road bases laid by the Romans which were durable enough to be made into fine highways by Napoleon. Roman roads in England were also improved and new highways were built under the impulse of the Industrial Revolution by the Scot, McAdam, who crushed stone for his roadbeds. In the United States, no military necessity such as the Napoleonic wars required the means of long overland transport; the abundant internal waterways, Indian trails for pack-horses and roads trampled out by herds of buffalo, later used by the sturdy Conestoga wagons, took the migrants west to the frontiers. What roads there were were usually "turnpikes," built and maintained by private enterprise, paid for by tolls. And most of these were bad enough. They became seas of mud in rainy seasons and were only passable if logs were laid across them making them what was known as "corduroy."

In preference to making roads, Americans dug canals where this was possible. When the railroads arrived, road-making virtually stopped dead. Across the continent, cities grew along the railroads as, once, they had grown along the rivers. Parts of the country which could not be reached by rail were simply out of luck; the railroads created many ghost towns and even caused certain considerable tracts of territory to lapse back into wilderness.

The European bicycling which began on the hard roads of France and England about 1870 was not, however, the kind of sport which would attract millions in democratic America. A few adventurous youths became expert at it here as well as abroad but it was a dangerous business except in the hands of an acrobat. The machine consisted of one large wheel, fifty-two inches in diameter and a very small wheel in the rear. The pedals were attached directly to the front wheel so that the rider had no benefit from reducing gears. When he fell, he fell nearly five feet so it was no wonder these trick contraptions were called "bone-breakers."

Eighteen years after the start of this perilous sport, an Irish veterinary named John Boyd Dunlop took out a patent for an invention which changed the whole face of the world. He did not know that the thing had actually been made and tried in England thirty-five years before and that the invention had died because no use had been found for it. But now the bicycle offered the chance. As soon as the invention was applied to it, the bicycle changed shape and became a world-wide fad. The invention was the pneumatic tire.

This extraordinary, elastic device is such a commonplace necessity today that it is hard to believe there was a time in which it did not exist. But if we can imagine a world without it, then we may also conjure up the excitement the invention caused when it first appeared. Already, in 1888, there were rumblings of a coming revolution in transportation. A few advanced thinkers in France and Germany were dedicating their lives to the design of new vehicles for the road which would no longer require the services of animals. More than ten years before this an American, George Selden, had applied for a patent on a buggy to be moved by the successive explosions of gas in a new kind of engine. To such visionary planners, Dunlop's brainstorm must have seemed heaven-sent.

It did not, however, take advanced thinking to see that bicyclists could now ride on air. Analyzing the effect of the tire, technicians saw the hundreds of little expanding and contracting vacuum cups the tire would use to grip the road. They saw the enlargement of the inflated tire at the point of contact presenting—but only at this point—a wider surface. They saw the possibility of shock absorption by the confined air. Inventive minds moved quickly after this: seeing the chance of utility in the trick machine on which men were risking their necks, they equalized the diameters of the wheels, devised a chain-and-sprocket mechanism to put the driving force in the rear wheel and by a proper ratio of the diameters of the sprockets reduce the rider's effort. These things were not all new. Gearing was ancient enough. The rear-wheel drive had, of course, been used on locomotives. The real bicycle novelty—which most distinctly marks its parenthood of the automobile—came in its contact, not of steel with steel, but of this relatively new substance, rubber, with a road's never entirely smooth surface.

The result of all the rapid thinking and planning of the bicycle enthusiasts was a machine which appeared in 1890 called the "safety." In more than sixty years of its existence, this bicycle has never changed except in unimportant details.

Americans give credit for its design to the Pope Manufacturing Company of Hartford, Connecticut, though something very like it seems to have appeared simultaneously in England and France. In any case the Popes, applying the interchangeable parts system, went quickly into the lead in production and were soon exporting the American machines to all parts of the world. By 1895, production by various American manufacturers came close to half a million a year and this for a machine costing at least $100 retail—then a considerable sum—was proof of the hypnotic hold the bicycle had on the American imagination.

Can we wonder at it? The only instrument of individual, physical freedom—the means of getting out, on your own, into the fresh air and the country, going where and when you liked, and as far as fancy (in the 1880's) might lead—was the horse. True, you could travel on trains and boats, but not privately, by yourself. You were always in the company of others, and you could go only where the rails or the water led after paying for your ticket. Only the horse satisfied the individual whim and (if you rode him) gave you exercise at the same time. But the horse had to be cared for—fed, sheltered, bedded down, groomed and harnessed or saddled. The horse was subject to disease and fatigue. He must be shod at intervals; wheedled and cajoled in his temperamental moments. Unless you lived on a farm where the horse plowed, cultivated and planted, he was a luxury. In the city he required expensive stabling and groom service: the ownership of horses by city-dwellers was a mark of real wealth.

The bicycle could be parked in the hallway of a tenement.

Beyond occasional doses of "Three-in-one" oil and the use of a rag to remove the mud, it required no care. Punctures or damage to the simple mechanism could be repaired at the nearest bicycle shop—there was one every few blocks. The fifty miles a day "tourist" cyclists rode would exhaust a horse, and, for the horse, the speed of the bicycle on the downgrade would not be possible.

For the first time, people living in city apartments were able to get to the country for a Sunday picnic in privacy and without expense. In rural districts bicyclists were able to explore places they hardly knew existed, with a minimum of effort. It was not long before clubs were organized— some for nature or geology study, some purely for recreation—and it was common to see groups of fifty or sixty bicyclists riding over the country roads: walking up the hills, perhaps, for rural highways were seldom graded, but coasting down with feet up on the front fork at what seemed like reckless speed.

One of the greatest blessings the bicycle brought was to women. Athletic exercises in those days were not for what was known as "the gentler sex." To girls and women everywhere the bicycle brought the means to health and muscle. It also favored a sensible change in feminine dress. Short skirts came in, and even the bloomers which look so hideous and clumsy to us in this day of clothes freedom were a relief from the cumbersome dust-gathering dresses of that late Victorian era.

In Paris, bicycling became an extremely fashionable activity in the middle 1890's and the so-called aristocracy of France could be seen daily in the Bois de Boulogne, enjoying polite conversation as they rode and exhibiting themselves to the surprised and admiring populace. Parisians went to absurd extremes in the bicycle craze, actually employing servants to care for their machines and establishing exclusive and expensive clubs dedicated to the new "sport."

In the larger eastern cities of the United States there were also clubs with luxurious restaurants and dressing rooms and, for unseasonable weather, large indoor riding rings because, rain or shine, people could not keep off their wheels. But bicycling soon became universal in America because quantity production and big markets made the "safeties" cheap and the advantages of riding to work to save carfare were soon appreciated by factory workers. Presently, too, they were adopted in quantity by police forces and Western Union. Today the situation is reversed: abroad the bicycle is the universal property of workers and lower-bracket businessmen; here the automobile has relegated it to children or to energetic vacationers.

By giving a new, individual freedom, a wider landscape and a new concept of distance, the bicycle prepared us psychologically for the automobile. But in two other ways its effect was physical and direct. One was in carrying the progress of the American interchangeable parts system a step further toward mass production.

With the spread of the bicycle craze, it soon became evident to repairmen the country over that parts must be standardized. No shop could be expected to carry different pedals, handle bars, sprockets and so on for all the different makes of bicycles. The idea that machine parts must be standardized and interchangeable spread, therefore, into corners of the country which the Whitney pattern had not yet penetrated. Small-town machine shops, small bicycle factories and even the tiny village repair shops were learning things which would make the more complex adjustments of car motors and transmissions easier. Equally important was the need of improving steel for a light machine which must stand hard usage. Steel tubing became an important article of manufacture but so too did case-hardened gear wheels and the components of ball bearings. New steel alloys for durable moving parts came in with the bicycle. Sheet steel and steel die presses were needed for mudguards and chain housing. The immense number of small accessories such as lamps, bells, brakes, tool kits and pumps which manufacturers vied with one another to exhibit at the great bicycle shows in New York and Chicago introduced new arts of gadgetry.

The other effect of the bicycle was to start a movement for good roads. This was highly organized. There were magazines devoted to nothing else; one called *Good Roads* had a wide circulation. Concerted propaganda, financed by bicycle manufacturers and clubs, worked on legislatures. The press soon took up the cry. Colonel Albert Pope, producer of the celebrated Columbia and Hartford bicycles, circulated a petition for government interest in roads and secured 150,000 signatures to it. He also was responsible for introducing courses in road engineering—on the McAdam principle—in the Massachusetts Institute of Technology.

The bicycle mania did not last long enough to advance the road reform far but it gave it the momentum to carry on when the mass production of motor cars made it absolutely necessary. The great enthusiasm for bicycling lasted, indeed, little more than twenty years, but it is hard to think of any influence on American social and mechanical history which, considering the brief life of the bicycling craze, was so powerful.

The bicycle, used for pleasure, introduced people to many new sights. City folk became familiar with farms, woods, streams and beaches of which they had known little. Often a bicycle ride led to a social gathering at lunch time. Many a romance began in the 'nineties on wheels, stimulated by the beauties of the landscape and the intimacy of riding together down lonely roads. There was a natural desire to remember these things, to have a tangible reminder of pleasant times incidental to this new sport.

One of the functions of art is to arrest the passage of time. It has been said that life would be intolerable without pictures which capture a passing mood, emotion or scene and hold it forever. In pictures, the past can be relived. The thrills of the bicycle era especially deserved mementos in sketches or photographs—or so the riders thought.

It would be too much to say that the bicycle was responsible for that other machine for pure pleasure which arrived in the same decade but certainly the two went often together and admirably served each other's purposes. The new machine was less utilitarian than the bicycle but it spread an epidemic of joy through the nation. It brought entertainment to young and old; to the ingenious youth who worked over noxious mixtures in a chemical lab and to the spinster who was hardly sufficiently skilled in technics to drive a nail or open a can. This was an optical device, the fruit of long patient progress in the securing of an image on a sensitized plate. It had a quick-moving shutter which, when a button was pressed, made two sharp little sounds. To its inventors, the machine in operation seemed to say "ko-dak."

Since the 1890's the machine has said those brief words countless billions of times in every remote spot of the world's surface. It has surprised wild animals drinking from lonely pools in hot African jungles. It has frightened naked savages who, looking up at the shutter's words, have run to hide from the little black box that was pointed at them. It catches our friends (and others) in comic positions and with the unstudied expressions that we call "candid." And its life has had no end. It is mass-produced today in delicate and precise forms by one of the world's most powerful industrial corporations and no doubt will be produced in some form as long as our civilization lasts.

Photography was invented in France in the late 1830's. For a half century it remained a difficult, elaborate business requiring either professional skill or long devotion by the amateur to chemical processes in a dark room. When glass replaced the metal of the daguerreotype, the coated, sensitized plates were exposed while still wet with a solution of silver nitrate. The camera was a large wooden box mounted on a tripod. For a long time, clear pictures could not be made of moving objects; there were, therefore, no photographs of horse races, ball games or animals (unless they could be mesmerized into posing) and candid shots were impossible because the subject always had time to become self-conscious while the long exposure took place.

In 1871, an ingenious Englishman named Maddox found that he could bind the sensitizer to the glass by a gelatin film and his plates could be used dry. This made photography easier for the amateur, but he still had to carry his heavy glass plates in frames protected from the light and insert them in the back of his camera without exposing them till they were in place and the shutter was opened. Also, the developing and hypo-fixing were still a headache unless you enjoyed that sort of thing.

Next, with the improvement of lenses and shutters, instantaneous photography arrived. This was a tremendous step forward. It brought some revolutionary discoveries. For instance, it was found that painters of galloping horses for thousands of years had invariably drawn their legs in positions which it was impossible for the running horse to assume. With the new photography also came news pictures. Always before, newspapers and weekly news magazines had illustrated their reporting with drawn pictures. When a reporter went to a fire or other dramatic event, the artist with his pencils and easel always went with him. The result was that the illustrations we find in the old *Harper's* and *Leslie's* weeklies were always partly creative—always slightly dramatized by the illustrator's fancy. So the instantaneous photograph gave us a new and sometimes disturbing view of life.

Still, photography was at best a semi-professional activity. There was still the glass plate with the gelatin film stuck to it. Then it occurred to an ingenious plate manufacturer that it might be possible to *use the film without the glass.*

Whether this was George Eastman's own idea or that of someone in his shop does not greatly matter for it was Eastman who made it work. He tried stripping the gelatin film off the glass but the result was too flimsy to use in a camera. So he attached it to paper. Then he rolled the paper on a spool. This was the first step which brought photography into the hands of the totally uninstructed amateur.

Eastman then manufactured a "roll-holder" which was a frame containing two spools and could be used in the cameras of the period. Each roll could be used for a hundred exposures by simply turning a handle to bring a fresh bit of sensitized paper behind the lens. When all the exposures had been made, the amateur photographer sent holder and all to Rochester and the Eastman factory developed and printed the pictures.

But Eastman was not long content with this advance. Its success made him want to go further. So he took the next step—a cheap, mass-produced, fool-proof camera. When it had been named "kodak," some creative genius invented the slogan: "You press the button, we do the rest." In the history of advertising no combination of name and slogan has had wider response. The little sentence was used for the captions of political cartoons, to point morals in sermons and as a catch-line in songs. It was translated into every language.

Eastman meant it. But his method of "doing the rest" soon made new technics necessary. The first system was to have the photographer send kodak and all to the factory after he had made his shots. Eastman was afraid to let the amateurs try to take the delicate paper rolls out of the camera. The kodak owners, however, of whom there was soon a large army, objected to the difficult and possibly hazardous business of shipping their precious toys back and forth. Also they wanted solid negatives which could not be made from the paper rolls. So next came an invention which not only completely simplified ordinary photography but made possible the entire new motion picture industry.

The controversy over who invented nitrocellulose film (commonly known as celluloid) lasted more than twenty-five years. Eastman thought it had been devised by a chemist in his laboratory named Reichenbach. But when Eastman film appeared on the market a New Jersey clergyman named Hannibal Goodwin claimed that he had applied for a patent on the same substance two years before Reichenbach. From 1889, then, until 1914 the battle raged and was finally won by the Goodwin interests when the court ordered Eastman to pay them five million dollars. In the meantime, however, countless millions of feet of Reichenbach-Eastman film had been made and sold rolled on spools protected by heavy, light-proof paper in the form we have it today. With these the loading and unloading of the kodak were easy enough and the amateurs could take the spools to the corner drugstore to have them developed. For the more ambitious photographic hobbyists the Eastman plant made compact and convenient developing and printing kits.

The coming of these two machines—the bicycle and the camera—for fun and freedom marks a new era in the life of the American people. From here on we see a succession of reforms to give workers more leisure to enjoy these and other pleasurable inventions. In the twentieth century, mass entertainment began with the movies and continued through radio into television and all of these were tied in with organized sport.

Today, perhaps, we have too much entertainment—too much diversion from increasingly serious realities which need our attention. It is pleasing, however, to look back occasionally to the beginnings of the enjoyment of life given us by mass production: to the long sunny days of riding into the country—small, happy events, still recalled, it may be, by old snapshots.

CHAPTER TWELVE

The Finished Map

WE COME at last to the climax of our story: the machine to which every step of our productive progress has led. Many Americans believe that, because it has become so universal here, the automobile was invented in the United States. Actually every basic part of it—engine, transmission, steering gear, differential—was invented abroad. What we did invent was a method of manufacturing cars in such quantity that we led the world in production and, indeed, produced some seventy-five per cent of the world's total. This extraordinary thing came to pass because of a belief that every American, regardless of his social status, race, color or even economic condition, was entitled to at least one automobile of his own. In point of fact, in the year 1953, there is one car in use for every four persons in the population.

The gasoline motor car that we know began in France and Germany. In America, early experiments were "horseless carriages"—strange monsters wholly different from what we call cars today. The Panhard and Levassor vehicle, however, which appeared in Paris in 1894, still looks like an automobile, while the Duryea, Haynes, King, Apperson, Maxim and Ford relics of the 1890's look like buggies from which the horses have run away in disgust, taking the shafts with them.

The Panhard had its engine in front under a hood and a V arrangement of cylinders. Its wheels were equipped with pneumatic tires and it had a steering wheel. Its transmission and differential were virtually the same as today's except for the most recent fluid or hydromatic drives.

American motor vehicles had their little engines in the rear or under the single seat. They usually had large rear wheels and small front ones with solid rubber or iron tires except in the rare cases in which bicycle wheels were used. (Ford, for example, in his first car, had the sense to do this.) Steering was by tiller. Transmission was by planetary gears and braking was on the rim in the majority of "horseless carriages" as it had been when the horse needed relief from pressure behind him when he was going down hill.

It is interesting to try to trace the reasons for these differences in the mentalities of the different peoples and of their inventors and engineers. Daimler in Germany and Levassor in France wanted to make beautiful machines which could move rapidly over the magnificent smooth and graded roads of the European continent regardless of cost. In real, basic inventions of such things as engines Europeans had always, as we have seen, been ahead of Americans. Their artisans had become engineers—students of such scientific subjects as statics, thermo-dynamics, metallurgy and mechanics—long before ours. But their fine results had been achieved largely by the labor of skilled workmen rather than by the machine sequences we had devised to take the place of men in our labor shortage.

The Panhard and Levassor car was as complete a symbol of all this as anything that had been produced in Europe in the nineteenth century. It was a hand-made beauty built for a hand-picked purchaser: a wealthy, educated, leisurely. sports-loving gentleman whose servants would keep his car cleaned, polished, oiled and repaired. Monsieur would pass easily from his bicycle to his automobile. No doubt he would keep his stable of fine horses but he would use these for show or for practice in the sport of horsemanship—not for serious travel or, as the French came to call it, *tourisme*. It is interesting, incidentally, to note how many words such as "automobile," "chassis," "chauffeur," "garage" are, like the motor car itself, of French origin.

In the United States in 1894, millions of miles of road were still exceedingly bad; the railroad had leapfrogged over them, so to speak, and many highways or turnpikes had been wholly abandoned. We did not, therefore, associate the bicycle—popular as it was—with long travel, which would necessarily take us over thoroughfares where only the horse could maneuver. Thus, when the motor-vehicle idea came to America, the minds of our mechanics at once jumped to carriages and, instead of making something new, they tried to persuade engines to move vehicles every detail of which was at variance with the whole automotive theory.

While Americans kept playing with the hybrid buggies, Europeans forged ahead with genuine motor cars. There was constant competition between France and Germany fostered by road races of more than three hundred miles—long for the day, but possible on the straight, smooth roads. Finally England, which had been held back by absurd laws reflecting public fear of road machines, swung into the contest and produced the beautiful Napier and Rolls-Royce cars containing the important advances of the six-cylinder engine and the multiple disc clutch. All this time America dropped behind: its best cars in the first years of the twentieth century were steam-propelled.

The steam engine as an automobile power plant was finally abandoned in the United States with the greatest reluctance. Compared with early gasoline motors, it was surprisingly efficient. Operating on the "flash" principle by which steam was generated with new speed, it won races for the White and Stanley cars and worked so silently without clutch or gear shift that it gained favor with thousands of Americans who saw the improperly designed gasoline cars stalled everywhere by the roadside. So it was only when Americans turned their eyes toward Europe and took over, one by one, the French, German and English inventions that it became possible for the gasoline automobile to swing into the lead in the United States.

But one of the strangest reasons of all which slowed American progress in what became the greatest triumph of mass production was a snobbish one. In the early days, the automobile was generally looked on as a "rich man's toy." The social élite of Newport, Long Island and New York—known in those days as the "Four Hundred"—started this prejudice by buying foreign cars. They started the sporting, reckless, daredevil fashion and the plain people would have none of it. When American cars were sold the market for them was therefore among the rich. The tendency of the horse-obsessed makers was to imitate the fancier vehicles such as phaetons, victorias and the light "traps" known as runabouts rather than buckboards or farm wagons. Even the first cheap car, the little Oldsmobile with its curved dashboard and low, pneumatic-tired wheels was thought "classy" and useless—having only one seat and no baggage provision—and the conservative farmers scorned it. To them, after all, the horse contained its own power plant, fueled by the farm's produce and contributing thereto a vital fertilizing function. To overcome this predilection an automotive machine had to be very good indeed, easy to operate, easy to repair, equal to steep grades and outrageous road surfaces and, above all, cheap.

The answer came in 1908 in a device called "Model T." With it the whole philosophy of mass production—technical and economic—reached its peak.

Whatever we may think of Henry Ford as a person—and he has been made into both a god and a demon—there is little question that he and Eli Whitney must stand as the two leading heroes of our American saga of production. In his whole thought and philosophy, no one has been more genuinely nineteenth-century American than Ford. He was a frontier product, governed by all the democratic impulses and prejudices which have leveled our society, destroyed classes and enforced the equality concept.

From early boyhood, Ford had two obsessions. One was with machinery. The other was with the "common man."

He seemed to understand mechanics by instinct. It was only necessary for him to look at any combination of wheels and levers to understand the whole of it. The reasoning by which he followed rotary movement through the most complicated sequence of gearing, translated reciprocating into rotary motion, estimated steam pressures, devised valve systems seemed instantaneous. While he was still a child he astonished his contemporaries by taking delicate watches wholly apart, reassembling them and improving their performance in the process. In his early teens he had a momentary desire to produce watches but abandoned it because he did not feel that he could make them by the tens of thousands at a cost of thirty cents each. Anything short of that was useless.

Unless you could make it possible for everyone to have a watch it was a waste of time to bother with it. The same powerful conviction gripped him when he had produced his first motor vehicle. The first time he drove his tiny, frail contraption, put together with his own hands in lonely night labor, he must have seen, in his mind's eye, the Detroit streets black with cars. Day by day as he worked against tough odds, the obsession grew. The automobile was *not* a rich man's toy. It was the poor man's utility. Its universal use was one of the obvious fruits of democracy. The idea that it was a luxury must be stepped on, crushed, at the start.

Ford knew that he must rouse public interest on a large scale in automobiles and in himself as their promoter. If large crowds could see the little cars in operation people would lose their fears of explosions and other accidents and also their belief that only a highly paid chauffeur could drive a car. He guessed that races were the quickest way to publicity. They would also appeal to the American speed impulse—well advanced by the 'nineties. He hated racing himself; he did not believe that high speed was a proper function of a motor car but he was willing to do anything to achieve his purposes. As a first step, it succeeded; the races in which he took part almost drove baseball off the sporting pages. One of the most valuable results was the creation of a large army of boy fans. It is interesting, thinking back over the later phases of American technology, to discover what an important part youngsters played in the acceptance of new devices. In radio broadcasting, for example, the boy "hams" with their crystal sets were the vanguard. Among the boys who watched the auto races of the early 1900's, hundreds became technicians or promoters; automotive engineers, administrators, salesmen or simple purchasers of the cars which had scared their parents.

Henry Ford's first large mechanical interest was in steam tractors, ponderous affairs as big as a small locomotive, which rumbled over the roads pulling threshing machines from farm to farm. At twelve, when one of these came to his father's farm at Greenfield, Michigan, Henry was so fascinated that farming never held him thereafter except when there was machinery to do the work. At eighteen, we know that he was apprenticed in a Detroit shop and that two years later he spent a year in southern Michigan setting up Westinghouse engines. His work with steam engines proved to him beyond any doubt that they were not for automobiles.

In this time he must have come abreast of the progress the American system had already made. He must have understood, intuitively, the prospects for mass production of machines. Very largely this must have come from a study of machine tools and bicycle parts. The public relations men who ghost-wrote Ford's "autobiographical" books have soft-pedaled this instructive period in the effort to persuade the American people that he created the whole of mass production out of the blue.

Ford was more than thirty when he built his first car in a dark shop adjacent to his modest home, working after hours. He was employed at the time in the Edison Illuminating Company. His fellow employees there were deeply interested in his experiments. Finally the great Edison himself found out about his car, encouraged him and thereupon became his life-long friend and hero. After eight years' work there during which all his spare time was spent in designing and building motor vehicles on his own, a group of people were willing to finance a company to manufacture Ford cars.

The ink was not yet dry on the organization papers of the Detroit Automobile Company—the French word had crossed the ocean—before Henry Ford was fighting with his backers. "The whole thought," he wrote, "was to make to order and to get the largest price possible for each car." Nothing could have been more contrary to Ford's obsession. He spent his time in this company, therefore, designing and building racers. These brought him celebrity and new backing. Four years later, in 1903, the Ford Motor Company was incorporated and $28,000 was invested in it.

All over again, the fight began. Henry was willing to go

along with his backers to a certain point. He had models A, B, C, F, K, N, R and S built, presumably to satisfy the stockholders. Actually he was experimenting. He was trying to find something which could be frozen, crystallized, made standard and produced forever. What he wanted was the simplest possible mechanism. It must have the fewest parts, be the easiest to understand and repairable with string and hairpins. It must be rugged, powerful, built to carry a family long distances up and down hills, over the roughest roads. There must be nothing fancy about it. The uglier the better. The ugly, hardworking look of it must shatter the rich man's toy prejudice forever. Ford's car must look what it was, utilitarian, the sort of thing millionaires would run away from. It must be painted black.

Once you get that frozen pattern you could spend all your time, money and effort, not improving the car, but improving the methods of turning it out. The idea of making a new model every year was uneconomical. It would mean a new annual cost of retooling your factory. If you went on producing the same thing year after year you could constantly cheapen its cost and so reduce its price.

The car Ford finally decided upon he called the Model T. When, in accordance with his plan, Ford lowered the price, the stockholders were worried.

"You mean to *reduce* the price every year?" they asked, in effect.

"That is my intention."

"How then will you make money?"

"By selling more cars."

"But your improved machinery will cost money. It will have to be financed. How will you do that?"

"By using the money I get for the cars to increase my plant."

"Then what happens to the profits?"

"They are to be plowed back into the works."

This was not orthodox business. Profits went to stockholders, not into machinery. But Ford had no faith in orthodox finance. He was suspicious of Wall Street. It was full of rich men—not good, common Americans. Their idea was to finance first and produce afterwards. Ford's way was to produce first and then finance your further production with what you made from your original sales. It did, of course, take a little capital, to launch even the Model T. But once it was launched it financed itself for eighteen years. Beyond the first $28,000 no outside investment was ever made.

But he could not tolerate the obstructing arguments of the stockholders. He felt their frustration as long as they lasted. Certain of them sued him and won. This brought the breaking point. Ford bought in all the stock. He paid more than a hundred million dollars for stock originally sold for $28,000. After that he had nothing more to worry about.

The Model T went into production in 1909. In 1913, production was a thousand cars a day. In 1915 the one-millionth Ford car came off a moving assembly line.

Ford did not invent the moving assembly line. It evolved gradually under long, constant experiment by such engineers as Walter Flanders, Charles Sorensen, William Knudsen and a host of technicians whose contributions have been forgotten. Ford himself watched everything they did. His genius lay in being able to say instantly when he saw something, "Yes, that's it!" rather than in dreaming up ideas. He was a recognizer of mechanical truths, not an originator of devices. He knew beforehand precisely what he wanted and when his engineers, stimulated by the broad terms of his desires, produced it he had only to say, "Yes, go on with that." And once a man was on the right track, Ford kept at him ruthlessly, unmercifully, to improve what he had begun, to step up speed, to produce more, more, always more. By the time he had won his fight for Model T as the one and only car, he knew that he could win every fight to produce it. As early as 1908, when Model T was still a hand-made showpiece, Ford set the goal of "a car a minute" and every man in his plant knew that the hard, driving work would never be relaxed before that incredible goal was reached.

It is a strange fact that, although work had been highly systematized and labor methodically divided in the making of guns and sewing machines, cars were still put together by skilled mechanics. That is because no one had ever thought of making *a lot* of automobiles. Who would buy them? With the announcement of the Model T, that was no longer a question. On every detail of the car Ford had guessed right. Simple, ugly, black, rugged: it was what people wanted. The company was swamped with orders. Enormous expansion would be necessary if half the demand was to be met. Henry Ford knew that it could be done by skilled mechanics. He knew, however, that there was such a thing in the world as mass production. So he got men who understood the system as it had been used to make other machines and had them install it for the biggest mass-production operation in history. To one engineer, he offered a twenty-thousand-dollar bonus over and above his salary if he could produce ten thousand cars the first year. The challenge was met. By the time the ten thousandth car came from the Ford factory the unique system had begun which, some five years later, became celebrated throughout the world.

It would have been impossible but for the work of all the pioneers we have met in this saga. Yet certain of its principles were quite new. The greatest of them was that the work should always be brought to the man—never the man to the work. Another—and one Henry Ford himself was especially proud of—was that the work should come to the man waist-high. No worker in the Ford plant was ever allowed to stoop to do a job once the system was installed.

It took six years to install it. It began in a small way. The first assembly line was for the fly-wheel magneto. The magneto contained many little parts and, originally, one man put them all together. When he had one magneto assembled he began on another. Each one took him twenty minutes. The assembly line broke the work into twenty-nine operations. The magneto moved from man to man on a conveyor and grew as it moved—each worker adding something. This cut the assembly time to thirteen minutes. Raising the line eight inches so there would be no stooping cut the time to seven minutes. Making the conveyor go a little faster cut it to five minutes. That meant that the magneto was put together four times as fast as before.

The motor assembly line came next and that required eighty-four separate little operations. Finally the engineers got to the point where they could try out the main or chassis assembly line which millions of people came from all over the world to see. Perhaps nothing in the whole of industry is more spectacular than this—although technically it is easier than some of the subassemblies.

The line was three hundred feet long. Along it were stationed teams of workers. At one end, the bare frames of the chassis were put on the conveyor. As each frame came opposite a team of workers they would add something— wheels, steering units, complete motors. These things were brought endlessly to the teams on overhead trolleys which had traveled from the subassembly lines, sometimes far away.

No one has described this better than Ford himself in his autobiography:

In the chassis assembling are forty-five separate operations or stations. The first men fasten four mud-guard brackets to the chassis frame; the motor arrives on the tenth operation and so on in detail. Some men do only one or two small operations, others do more. The man who places a part does not fasten it— the part may not be fully in place until after several operations later. The man who puts in a bolt does not put on the nut; the man who puts on the nut does not tighten it. On operation number thirty-four the budding motor gets its gasoline; it has previously received lubrication; on operation number forty-four the radiator is filled with water, and on operation number forty-five the car drives out. . . .

The thrill with which the crowds of visitors watched this magic parade cannot be described. Ford had a good deal of the showman about him. He wanted the world to see this spectacle, not simply as a circus show but as a practical working demonstration of how it was possible to put this luxury in the hands of all his countrymen. "I will build," he said in his first announcement of the Model T, "a motor car for the great multitude." By 1924, the multitude had grown to ten million. Before the Model T died in 1927, the Ford Motor Company had sold fifteen million cars.

And Henry Ford kept his promise of reducing his price. Except for the war years, he cut it every year. The Model T started at $950 in 1909. By 1912 it was down to $780, by 1913 to $600, by 1916 to $440 and by 1917 to $360. It hit rock bottom at $290 in 1926. This was precisely what mass production was meant to do but perhaps Ford was the only industrialist who carried it all the way. Year after year the others kept saying that it was unorthodox business and predicted Ford's downfall, yet year after year his profits increased and he ended by making more money than any manufacturer in the history of the world.

In 1914, he formulated part two of his philosophy, namely, that workers ought to be able to buy what they produced. It was in that year that he established the minimum wage of five dollars a day. Such pay was undreamed of in any manufacturing plant in the world. It more than doubled his previous wage. The shock of the news divided the public into two parts, one which believed him a philanthropist of supernatural goodness and generosity and the other which pronounced him definitely and finally insane. Yet the scheme worked. The workers improved their performance and they bought Ford cars. And the profits went steadily up.

What the public did not understand was that all this was possible because of the economies mass production had brought about. Every day some kind of waste was cut down —waste of time, energy, motion, materials. Every day some process was shortened. Every year some new by-product was created out of something that had been thrown away. Even the sweepings of the floors were salvaged. Every scrap of metal went into the making of new metal, every bit of paper went to a paper mill to be ground into pulp for cardboard packing boxes.

Money accumulated to a point which worried Henry. After he had bought in all the stock, the profits, of course, all came to him and there was too much. He could not plow it back; the Model T plant needed no further expansion. It was then that he conceived the idea of what came to be known as the Ford empire.

In the beginning the Ford company had bought many of the parts for the Model T. This included steel castings and forgings, tires, cloth for the top, upholstery and many other things. The Ford empire was developed to produce everything that went into a car in Ford plants and to produce it from the basic raw materials. Ford bought iron mines, shipped the ore on his own boats to his immense new River Rouge works and there smelted it, cast pig iron and made that into steel ingots in huge open-hearth furnaces. He rolled the steel in hot and cold automatic continuous strip mills for his bodies and various parts which needed sheet steel. In his own foundries he made die castings to be machined into moving parts. He bought forests and made his own lumber, rubber plantations and built at Rouge a tire plant, he planted acres of flax and soybeans for natural and synthetic yarn for his fabric. He constructed a complete glass works and in it installed the first continuous plate glass process in the world.

Ford then abolished warehouses and made his whole empire into a network of moving assembly lines, so to speak, with everything in continuous motion over much of the world. Everything was geared to the final assembly: freight trains, steamships, trucks all bringing materials to be processed and made into automobiles, the final product to be at the assembly line at precisely the moment that the chassis of a Ford car arrived at that point. The result was that materials were not stored at the plant: they were forever moving through lakes and rivers, being worked on in rubber plantations in South America, Michigan lumber mills, Lake Superior ore deposits or deposits in Europe or Asia of rare metals for steel alloys; soybean plantations in Michigan and Pennsylvania coal mines. And then all over the United States and in England, Ireland, Sweden, Finland, Denmark, Holland, Belgium, France, Germany, Spain, Portugal, Italy, Egypt, South Africa, Australia, India, Malaya and Japan the company built branch plants, mostly for assembly of parts shipped from Michigan. In this "empire" mass production advanced to its furthest point.

The empire was largely a product of the 1930's. The Model T, however, died in 1927.

Why did it die? Why must this thing which had become a veritable part of American folklore come to an end?

Specifically it was killed by a competitor known today as Chevvy. The real reason for its decline, however, was a change in tastes caused, perhaps, by a kind of growing up of the American people. In this restive advance to maturity came a desire for something a little smoother, more powerful, more "refined." Ford had guessed right in 1908 when the ordinary American had refused the rich man's toy. But in 1927 another generation had gone to college, become more prosperous, more "urbane"—which seems to be a quality achieved by living in cities instead of lonely farm communities. College boys and girls laughed at Dad's "flivver" as they called Model T or "Tin Lizzie." Some neighbor was getting a Chevrolet or a Dodge: shouldn't we "keep up with the Joneses"?

It was all a perfectly democratic process. Give a man a luxury and it breeds in him a desire for something still more luxurious. With the American system he can have it. As competition in automobiles grew and the beautiful machines of Chrysler, General Motors, Packard, Studebaker and the others flashed past the old, ugly, standard Fords on the road, drivers struggling to manage the planetary transmissions with foot pedals followed these visions with longing eyes. Finally the big used car market which had grown to vast proportions made it possible to buy a not quite new low-slung, quiet and fast job for even less than a new Model T.

For Henry Ford this was tragedy. His whole idea had been against changing his model. But, in a sense, the world had passed him by. Rivals, using his methods, were producing something that fitted into the new world for almost as low a price as his. Chevrolet, for the "common man," was the first step toward that new world. So when Ford car sales dropped to a dangerous low, Henry let himself be persuaded. It was, perhaps, the first time in his life that he admitted he was wrong. Production of T was stopped in May, 1927.

It took a year to prepare the River Rouge plant for the new design which was called Model A. There had to be new tools throughout. Since Model A, there have been almost yearly changes. The mechanics of mass production went on improving year by year. Unfortunately the economics of mass production did not. The Ford practice which worked so happily during the high, wide and handsome days of the 1920's no longer worked. Depression and government regulation which it necessitated and finally the disruption of war made it impossible to reduce the prices every year.

Perhaps this was a reason why Henry Ford became more interested in other things than in passenger cars. He went in for tractors and airplanes and the building of museums and historical collections. Yet he must, to the end, have been proud of having carried the American system to its highest point in the manufacture of his standard automobile and of having proved the principle that mass production makes possible a progressive lowering of costs—and proved it with a force and finality that no one before or since has been able to do. The temper of the times and the climate of a free economy were, of course, powerfully in his favor.

The mass-produced automobile has changed our map so completely that it would hardly be recognizable to a Rip Van Winkle who might wake today from a fifty years' sleep. We know that, officially, the great American frontier closed in the 1880's. Since then, however, the motor car has filled in the vacant spaces left by the old frontier's movement: indeed, it has made what might be called new frontiers. Along the network of highways the cars created, ghost towns have come to life, new communities have grown to great size. Commerce of every kind from the humble fruit stand to the large taverns and "motels" has blossomed in places that were dark swamps scarcely more than a generation ago. The America the railroad built is only a fraction of the America we know. The picture puzzle pieces which the car has fitted into our map are countless. Half a century ago the greater part of our country was unknown and inaccessible to the large majority of Americans. In the 1950's there is no corner so remote that it may not be explored with little effort or expense.

This has come about as a consequence of one man's obsession with a little, black, snub-nosed, noisy and odorous machine, shied at by horses, barked at by dogs and sneered at by little boys who shouted "Git a horse" until, finally, the man made one of them come off his line every ten seconds and fifteen million Americans were driving them. Certainly, the job was an assembly of a hundred inventions by other men; surely, this genius could not have moved a step without the work of the thousands of his predecessors since Eli Whitney. And, possibly, if Henry Ford had not made this revolution someone else, in time, would have.

The fact remains that he did.

CHAPTER .THIRTEEN

Conclusion

A<small>ND THE FUTURE</small>? That is something this book must not guess at. We have been interested in the past and in understanding why we are where we are today. That is something it is vitally important for every American to know. If he thinks he has dropped into a world which was ready made for him by a miracle, he is in danger. To those of us who find life as easy as that there is trouble ahead. The acceptance of all our push-button existence as if there were no history of centuries of toil, patience, sweat and pain behind every item of it often makes men believe that hard work is unnecessary. Too many Americans are falling into that error simply through ignorance. The Spanish philosopher Ortega y Gasset calls this the mentality of the "mass man" who is swept along by the rapid currents he finds himself in without inquiring about their origin.

The production of goods and machines which is so uniquely American is what has made it possible to grow as quickly as we have and still remain a single integrated nation. But it has brought along some dubious things with it.

By making many things which are all alike, it has made us think alike. Someone has said that the thoughts of Americans are interchangeable like the parts of their gadgets. Mass production required so much capital that it has brought about the merging of big businesses creating bigger business which is said to drive small business to the wall. It is also said that the use of so many automatic machines and such minute subdivision of labor removes all skill and therefore takes away a man's pride in his work.

All of these things are partly true. None of them seems conclusive when stacked up with the great benefits. The standardization argument is answered by the fact that mass production is becoming more flexible all the time. Already engineers have designed machine sequences which can be adjusted to new products without the tremendous cost of retooling. The monopolies or near-monopolies formed by merging may be justified if they lower prices. A monopoly is not, in itself, an evil. The evil comes in the abuse of a monopoly—when it is used to raise prices because there is no competition, rather than to lower them which should be the result of its economies.

Henry Ford said:

I have heard it said . . . that we have taken skill out of work. We have not. We have put in skill. We have put a higher skill into planning, management, and tool building, and the results of that skill are enjoyed by the man who is not skilled. . . . Our skilled men are the tool-makers, the experimental workmen, the machinists and the pattern makers. They are as good as any men in the world—so good, indeed, that they should not be wasted in doing that which the machines they contrive can do better.

This statement is debatable unless there is a chance for the intelligent assembly-line worker to graduate into the more skillful and creative positions. But today industrialists are growing more and more aware of this necessity and encouraging workers to go to night school and learn to become technicians and engineers.

One of the charges brought against mass production is that it makes possible wars on a scale far beyond all parallels in history. This is true. Mass destruction has become as easy as mass building. The new techniques amplify everything they touch. But they are capable of amplifying good as well as evil. A machine or a thousand machines cannot be either bad or virtuous. We sometimes forget this because the line of machines is so long. Behind every machine there is another machine and the long sequence of them stretches to the point where we sometimes cannot see the man behind them all. But there is always a man there. He can control the whole sequence by a touch of his hand. And it is the man and only the man who is capable of right and wrong.

Whatever we may think of it, it is safe to assume that, after this century and a half of development, mass production is here to stay. In its last phases its strides have been long and rapid—so fast indeed that our minds have scarcely yet caught up. But when we learn to take it in our stride—no longer as a "marvel" but as a simple fact of life—using it for those purposes for which it is most useful; allowing skilled work and even handicraft still to take their rightful place in the making of beautiful and various things in small quantities and, above all, finding ways to keep it from causing unemployment, stultifying active minds and "freezing" thought into rigid patterns, it can advance the whole of civilization as it has played its vital part in the conquest and integration of our continent.

Index